THE PSYCHIATRIST
AND THE LAW

THE
PSYCHIATRIST
AND THE LAW

Winfred Overholser, M.D., Sc.D.

Superintendent, Saint Elizabeths Hospital
Professor of Psychiatry, George Washington University
School of Medicine
Past President, American Psychiatric Association

HARCOURT, BRACE AND COMPANY
NEW YORK

TO MY WIFE

CONTENTS

PREFACE

THE AMERICAN PSYCHIATRIC ASSOCIATION established in 1952, through the efforts of Dr. Gregory Zilboorg of New York City, the Isaac Ray Award, to be given annually to that individual who, in the judgment of the Award Committee, "is most worthy by reason of his contribution to the improvement of the relations of Law and Psychiatry." The awardee is expected to lecture at some university which has both a law school and a medical school.

I am deeply grateful for the honor conferred on me in being selected as the first recipient of the award and for the privilege accorded me by President Conant and Deans Griswold and Berry of presenting my lectures in November, 1952, at Harvard University, where I received my academic education.

For my early interest in the field of forensic psychiatry I am largely indebted to Professor Sheldon Glueck, of the Harvard Law School; Mr. Melvin M. Johnson, formerly Professor and Dean of the Boston University School of Law; the late Herbert C. Parsons, for many years Commissioner of Probation for the Commonwealth of Massachusetts; and the late George M. Kline, for many years Massachusetts Commissioner of Mental Diseases.

In preparing these lectures I have been greatly aided by the advice of Mr. Justice Felix Frankfurter, of the United States Supreme Court; Judge Justin L. Miller, formerly of the United States Court of Appeals for the District of Columbia, and Professor Glueck. To these men, and to my early guides and mentors, I gladly express my gratitude and obligation.

My office staff, Miss L. M. Drennan, Mrs. Brunhilde M. Knott, and Miss Martha Marine, and the Medical Librarian of Saint Elizabeths Hospital, Miss Elizabeth Reavis, have been of inestimable assistance in compiling and typing the manuscript.

It is my hope that the comments presented in the following pages may prove a small contribution to a closer understanding and co-operation between the practitioners of the law and of psychiatry.

WINFRED OVERHOLSER, M.D.

Saint Elizabeths Hospital
Washington, D.C.

I

THE SUBSTANCE OF
PSYCHIATRY

ISAAC RAY, in honor of whose memory this lecture-ship has been established, was one of the great American psychiatrists. Born in Beverly, Massachusetts, in 1807, he attended Phillips Andover Academy, Bowdoin College, and the Bowdoin and Harvard Medical Schools. He received his degree in medicine from Bowdoin in 1827 and subsequently the degrees of Master of Arts from Bowdoin in 1846 and Doctor of Laws from Brown in 1879. He practiced medicine in Portland and in Eastport, Maine, became superintendent of the Maine State Hospital at Augusta in 1841, and in 1847 superintendent of Butler Hospital in Providence, Rhode Island. He was one of the founders of the Association of Medical Superintendents of American Hospitals for the Insane, now known as the American Psychiatric Association, and President from 1855 to 1859. He retired in 1867 and moved to Philadelphia, where he lived until his death in 1881. He was a most prolific writer in the field of psychiatry, particularly on the legal aspects of that specialty, and hardly a year of his professional life passed without one or more original contributions appearing in the literature.

His chief claim to fame is the fact that in 1838, while a country practitioner in Eastport, Maine, he published *A Treatise on the Medical Jurisprudence of Insanity,*

[3]

the first systematic treatise on this topic to appear in the English language. The book went through six editions in this country, as well as one (1839) in England, and at the time of his death a seventh was under way. For many years the book was quoted by courts of last resort, both in this country and in England. A New England pioneer in the field of forensic psychiatry, he has been succeeded in New England by a line of workers in the same field, a line which includes such names as William Healy, the pioneer in psychiatric studies of juvenile delinquency and for many years the head of the Judge Baker Guidance Center; Professor Sheldon Glueck of the Harvard Law School; Dr. Victor V. Anderson, the founder of the first adult court clinic in the United States (in Boston); Dr. L. Vernon Briggs, the father of the famous Briggs Law; Dr. Douglas A. Thom, one of the early workers in the child guidance movement; and Drs. Abraham Myerson and A. Warren Stearns, able champions of forensic psychiatry at its best.

Doctor Ray began his preface to his treatise in 1838 thus: "Few, probably, whose attention has not been particularly directed to the subject, are aware, how far the condition of the law relative to insanity is behind the present state of our knowledge concerning that disease. While so much has been done, within a comparatively short period, to promote the comfort of the insane . . . it is both a curious and a melancholy fact, that so little has been accomplished towards regulating their personal and social rights, by more correct and enlightened principles of jurisprudence. While nations are vying with one another in the excellence of their public establishments for the accommodation of this unfortunate class of our fellow-men, and physicians are every year publishing some instance of an unexampled proportion of cures, we remain perfectly satisfied with the wisdom of our predecessors in everything relative to their legal relations. This, no doubt, is mainly the fault of medical men themselves, who have neglected to obtain for the results of their researches, that influence on the law of insanity which they have exerted on its pathology and therapeutics." These words, though written 114 years ago, can well be repeated today with equal truthfulness.

When Ray wrote his masterpiece, psychiatry was hardly known as a specialty. Indeed, the word was not then, nor until long after, in general use. The specialist in mental medicine confined his efforts largely to the mental hospital or to the courtroom, and very little was known of the nature of mental processes. Such data concerning mental activity as were then thought to be facts we now consider to have been incorrect. The specialty of psychiatry has developed with the increasing knowledge of the nature of mental mechanisms, and we have sound reason to believe that we know much more concerning the causation of behavior, normal and abnormal, than was known 100 years ago.

Psychiatry as we know it today has been defined by Sir David K. Henderson, Professor of Psychiatry at Edinburgh, as "that branch of medicine which deals with those individuals, who from a combination of circumstances, constitutional or acquired, are unable to adapt themselves satisfactorily to their particular situation in life because of certain signs and symptoms, certain maladjustments, which may or may not require treatment in the home, the school, the college, the factory, the clinic, nursing home, or hospital." Since the concern of psychiatry is with the treatment of maladjustments and with the restoration of the ailing to health it follows that it is interested likewise in the wellsprings of human behavior among the vast "normal" majority of mankind, and in the prevention, so far as possible, of mental disorder.

Law, like psychiatry, deals very largely with the conduct of human individuals and their relations with their fellows. This is equally true, whether we consider contests between individuals over property rights, suits for damages, cases involving divorce and annulment, the validity of wills, deeds, or contracts, the commitment of the mentally ill to hospitals, or the various types of cases dealt with under the criminal law. It is hard indeed to conceive of a legal case which does not involve the behavior or the motivations of some person; even in United States v. One Book called *Ulysses,* the book was not written or imported without human intervention! It is thus entirely reasonable to expect that psychiatry would have an interest in the administration of the law, and that those charged with the law's administration should desire to benefit by psychiatric progress.

In spite of this apparently reasonable expectation, it is a fact that the law still proceeds on the basis of psychological assumptions which are not in line with prevailing psychiatric points of view. Furthermore, not only has the law in certain fields been extremely hesitant to keep up with psychiatric progress or even to lag at a reasonably short distance, but some lawyers and judges have been extremely critical of the findings of psychiatry and have shown the greatest reluctance to learn.

It is sometimes said that the reason for this hesitation is that the law is in essence bound to be, to some extent at least, retrospective, that it must be based upon well-established precedents and upon generally accepted attitudes on the part of the public, if it is to have that force and vigor which it should have. The unfortunate results which flow from a situation in which a law is out of line with the public's attitude are well remembered by many of us in connection with the unlamented "experiment, noble in purpose," of Prohibition. Because that law was not in accord with the sentiments of the majority of the people of the United States it failed lamentably, and its failure is blamed by many for a lower standard of respect for the law than had previously prevailed. The law, then, should attempt to follow rather than to lead, although it is also true that it should at least follow at a sufficient distance to be able to keep in sight of the rest of the procession!

The law *has* made progress in accepting the discoveries of science, a fact which must be admitted by the most hardened critic. An excellent example of the acceptance by the law of the advances of science is the present general recognition of the scientific facts relating to blood grouping, not only in tests of non-paternity but also in the identification of blood stains. I say a *general* recognition. It is a fact, of course, that as recently as 1946 [1] the highest court of California affirmed, on entirely legalistic grounds, a verdict by which a well-known actor was held by a jury to be the father of an illegitimate child, even though the uncontradicted blood grouping tests made by several experts proved conclusively as a matter of scientific fact that he could not have been the father. Fortunately, most states now recognize that scientific fact is more dependable than the whims or sympathies of a jury, and a recent similar paternity judgment in Maine, for example, was reversed on this ground. [2] Another recent development of scientific evidence is the use of quantitative reports of the alcoholic content of the breath or blood of persons accused of being intoxicated. Recently, too, the results of electro-encephalographic tests, the so-called "brain waves," have been admitted in the occasional criminal case. The results of the use of the "lie detector" are as yet rarely admitted in court, although the instrument is progressively proving its value in police interrogation.

We must look, then, for some further reason why psychiatry, this particular specialty of medicine, has not been so readily accepted by the law as have the other branches of the medical science and art. Some of these reasons are historical, some of them are intrinsic in the specialty, and some of them (if a mere psychiatrist may be so bold) may be intrinsic in the critics.

There is nothing new about mental disorder. We find records of it in the Egyptian papyri and in the Old Testament. Excellent early descriptions of depres-

[1] References will be found on pp. 135-142.

sion, mania, dotage, and drunkenness are found in some of the oldest literature known. The early explanations of this peculiar behavior were demonological, although the Greeks developed a naturalistic point of view concerning causation and treatment, and used such words, still in use today, as mania, melancholia, and paranoia. After the beginning of the Christian era, however, the theological point of view gained the ascendancy, and the care of the mentally ill (if it may be called that) was left almost entirely to the clergy; mental disorder was looked upon as essentially due to possession by evil spirits and as therefore treatable by exorcism. The trials for witchcraft and the executions of countless thousands of persons who by our present standards were mentally deranged but who were then considered witches, constitute a black chapter in the history of human behavior. A few physicians were daring enough to point out the true nature of the condition from which the so-called witches suffered, but the statements of one of the most vigorous, Johannes Weyer, were very casually dismissed by the Saxon Criminal Code of 1572 with the statement that they were not very important "since he is a physician and not a jurist." It was not until the time of Pinel (during the French Revolution) that psychiatry was set forth again as belonging in the field of medicine, rather than in that of theology or philosophy. Pinel is best remembered as a reformer, the man who struck off the chains of the mental patients at the Salpêtrière. He was far more than that, however. He was an astute, widely read, and well-trained physician who set himself to study the cases of mental disease, in his words "noticing successively every fact, without any other object than that of collecting materials for further use and endeavoring to divest [himself] of the influence of [his] own prepossessions and the authority of others." Pinel wrote a treatise on mental disorder in 1801, and although an Italian physician, Chiarugi (1793), had actually antedated Pinel both in writings and in practice by a few years, it is from Pinel that we date the recognition of psychiatry as a specialty of medicine.

Little was known in Pinel's time or indeed for a good while after it, of the causation of mental disorders or of their treatment. Much stress was laid on the presumed abnormal condition of the brain substance itself or disturbances in its function by reason of presumed changes in blood flow and pressure. It was recognized, however, that emotional factors could be important, both in the causation and in the so-called "moral" treatment of these illnesses. The German, Kraepelin, and later the Swiss, Bleuler (the originator of the term schizophrenia), in the latter part of the nineteenth and earlier part of the twentieth century wrote extensively, classified types of mental disorder, and emphasized the close relationship of mental disorder to physical factors, whether organ defect, heredity, metabolic changes, or disorders of internal secretion. Even, however, with the researches of Kraepelin and Bleuler, very little was known of the mechanisms of mental disorder or indeed of the mechanisms of everyday behavior. Psychiatry still was practiced almost exclusively in the mental hospitals, with occasional incursions into the courtroom. The modern era in psychiatry began shortly after the turn of the century with the work in Europe of Sigmund Freud and the translation of some of his writings into English by A. A. Brill in 1909 and with the contributions in this country of William Alanson White and of Adolf Meyer, for many years Professor of Psychiatry at the Johns Hopkins University and the exponent of the "psychobiological" concept of psychiatry.

In view of the many misunderstandings and misinterpretations which still exist, many of them handed down through centuries, it seems proper to give a very brief summary of the present views of the make-up of personality and of some of the disorders to which it is subject.[3] What we generally term "mind" is an abstraction, an inclusive word which signifies the sum total of the ways in which the individual acts as a whole in response to the stimuli, internal and external, which are constantly playing upon him. Mental activity, then, is merely one aspect of biological functioning. The mind does not have a separate entity, nor does it exist in a vacuum, separately from the body. The various parts of the physical body, the muscles, the glands, the sensory and other organs, are unified through the action of the nervous system. The central organ of this system is the brain, an extremely complicated structure which deals with the perceptions of the inner needs of the individual, receives the stimuli from the outside world, responds to those stimuli by motor phenomena of various sorts, and stores the various impressions which it has received. This latter phenomenon is referred to as memory. By means of memory the effects of training are accumulated and various associations are set in motion, some of which at least appear to result in what is known as logical thought. On the basis of these memories and previous impressions judgment is developed. Since the richness of the associations and memories is an important factor in judgment and the other so-called higher functions, it is clear that organic damage to the brain may be expected to have an effect upon them. This damage may be due to external injury, to failure of development, whether congenital or resulting from early infection, to the later development of infections of the brain itself, to circulating toxins in the blood stream, as from fever or from drugs, and from degenerative changes due to advancing years, that is, senility and arteriosclerosis. Damage from any of these causes may be expected to bring about changes, temporary or permanent, in the personality, that is, the total functioning of the individual in his conduct, in his judgment, and in his ability to respond to the stimuli of the outside world; in short, in his mind.

In addition to the brain and the nerves which run to it conveying sensation, or which emanate from it conveying motor impulses (the so-called central nervous system), we find another very important system, the autonomic or vegetative, a system which functions almost entirely independently of our volition or consciousness. This portion controls such functions, for example, as the bodily temperature, blood pressure, digestion and excretion, and the various glands, both of internal and external secretion. It acts as the mediator between the emotions and the functioning of the so-called involuntary organs. It is by means of this system that we experience such phenomena as goose-flesh, blushing, sweating from fright, and so on. It controls what Cannon, the great Harvard physiologist, has referred to as homeostasis; it is, in other words, through the functioning of this part of the nervous system that the bodily functions referred to as "vegetative" are kept in balance so far as possible, despite the changes in the external or the internal environment. The symptoms produced by the functioning of the autonomic nervous system under unusual conditions of stress are important from the point of view of what is today known by the somewhat objectionable term of psychosomatic medicine; the "traumatic neuroses" constitute one type of these disorders.

Freud schematically divided mental functioning into three spheres. The first he referred to as the "id," comprising the storehouse of biological forces, devoted in part to self-preservation and reproduction, not unlike the *"élan vital"* of Bergson, the drive to live. To this drive he applied the term "libido"—a word which because of its earlier associations has been responsible for much misunderstanding. The second category he termed the ego, that is, the integrative part of the personality, which acts as mediator among the id on the one hand, the superego (of which more in a moment), and outside reality. The third he referred to as the superego, a concept roughly similar to conscience, the unconscious part of the personality, resulting largely from early identification with parents and other authoritative figures, which acts as the guide to conduct and stands ready to produce psychological difficulties if its dictates are violated. These are not localized in parts of the brain and, indeed, have

only a schematic existence. They are convenient ab-
stractions, however, and serve a useful clinical purpose
in discussing the deviations of personality and, indeed,
the motivations of the normal.

Certain of our functions are carried on at what we
know as the conscious level, but consciousness is only
the surface phenomenon of mental functioning. The
important point which Freud emphasized was that impressions, experiences, teachings, many of them consciously forgotten, are nevertheless stored in what he
referred to as the unconscious. In one of his earlier
books, *The Psychopathology of Everyday Life,* Freud
points out to what an extent we are driven by our unconscious in our everyday life, waking and sleeping. Unpleasant experiences may be repressed, so that they are
apparently forgotten, yet they may come out in disguised form, causing phobias, tics, anxieties, and various
neurotic and even psychotic manifestations. These con-
stellations with a heavy emotional charge are referred
to as complexes. Even slips of the tongue are found to
have an unconscious emotional basis and not to be entirely "accidental." Needless to say, everyone has complexes; it is how one deals with them or how they deal
with him that is important.

One thing which the growing child soon learns is
to distinguish between himself and the outside world
with its demands. This sense of reality which one devel-
ops is constantly in use for testing one's desires and instinctual drives. The human being is in a constant state
of conflict between his desires, such as those for sex, for
food, for acclaim, approbation, and power on the one

hand, and the requirements of the reality-situation on the other. The demands of reality, including the generally accepted rules of behavior, are incorporated to a considerable extent into the superego, so that when there is a violation of the dictates of the superego, feelings of guilt arise. Despite the superego, however, we may observe under the stress of strong emotion, especially fear or rage, or of the instinctual demands, as hunger, reactions of a primitive, socially unacceptable type, such as serious assaults or other aggressive acts. The relation of such instinctual "break-throughs" to the fine-spun legal theories of premeditation and intent will not be elaborated at this point.

Feelings of guilt may manifest themselves in depressions or states of anxiety, or they may be translated by the process of projection into ideas of reference or paranoid delusions, feelings that other persons are the guilty ones, rather than the individual himself. If this sense of reality is seriously impaired we speak of the individual as mentally ill. In the extreme psychoses, that is, in the more disturbed forms of mental disorder, we find very serious disturbances in this field. No one ever achieves during life a state of complete equilibrium, emotionally or physically. This truth was well stated, with that insight which we often find in the novelist, by Samuel Butler, in his *Way of All Flesh,* as follows: "All our lives long, every day and every hour, we are engaged in the process of accommodating our changed and unchanged selves to changed and unchanged surroundings; living, in fact, is nothing else than this process of accommodation; when we fail in it a little we are stupid, when we

fail flagrantly we are mad, when we suspend it tem-
porarily we sleep, when we give up the attempt alto-
gether we die."

Life is always a compromise, a process of adjustment,
and not all the forces which are exerted upon any one
person can be resolved. Therefore, defenses of one sort
or another are necessary against these various conflicts.
We may have, for example, repression, that is, a denial
of the existence of a given situation. More commonly,
perhaps, we tend to blame others for our shortcomings,
and not infrequently to "find" in others undesirable or
blameworthy traits which we attempt consciously or unconsciously to repress in ourselves. This latter reaction
of projection is exhibited in extreme form in the paranoid psychotic, who feels himself the victim of various
plots and persecutions. During the recent war what is
known as acute homosexual panic was often observed.
In this condition young men who had a certain homosexual component found, in the situations in which
they were exposed at close range to groups of persons
of their own sex, that this component of their instinctual drives was brought nearer to a conscious level. To
admit to themselves that they had these homosexual
urges, however, would be too painful, and therefore
they took flight into a state of panic and fear in which
they characteristically heard voices (hallucinations) ac-
cusing them of homosexual activities.

Again we may have the defense of overcompensation,
what is commonly known as "leaning over backwards."
Rationalization is another extremely common phenomenon, an attempt to explain satisfactorily to one's self,

but often without real success, why one feels and desires as one does. Another more primitive type of reaction is to retreat along the lines of earlier development, that is, to regress, so that we may find childish types of thinking and acting or even, in extreme psychoses, the assumption of intra-uterine postures; these are especially noted in schizophrenia, or "dementia praecox." Again reactions may be formed, such as the compulsive type, in which the subject may be involuntarily driven to commit acts which are forbidden; this symptom is of interest in connection with the disputed legal question of "irresistible impulse." Kleptomania is an example. Various types of obsessional thinking or phobias may be developed, and some of the conflicts may be translated into various physical symptoms such as palpitation, digestive disturbances, tics, or even into hysterical paralyses or anesthesias. It should not be thought that these defenses are developed consciously and intentionally, nor that they are necessarily adopted for purposes of conscious deceit (malingering). They are protective mechanisms which develop for the most part quite unconsciously. They are nonetheless extremely potent, and sometimes resistant to treatment.

Freud has often been accused of having attributed all of the abnormalities of behavior to sexual disturbances. That accusation is inaccurate, but the fact cannot be gainsaid that the sexual drive is an extremely important one and that on account of the many taboos with which it is associated it is one which we often find at the basis of emotional difficulties. The generally accepted theory of what is known as psychosexual development, very concisely stated, is as follows: The young child is interested first in himself and in his mother, the source of his nourishment and of attention. He may develop such an attachment to her that he vies with his father for her attention; this is referred to as the Oedipus situation. Indeed, some men, thanks to what Philip Wylie has termed "Momism," never develop emotionally much beyond this stage. Somewhat later, in the pre-adolescent stage, the boy or girl goes through a period of scorning the opposite sex, hero-worships his or her leaders, has "crushes" on playmates of the same sex, and sometimes makes sexual experiments with them. This is referred to as the homosexual stage of psychosexual development, without any necessary implication of overt homosexual activity. The heterosexual or adult stage sets in about puberty, with developing interest in the opposite sex. It should be pointed out that this schematic development refers to the psychologic attitudes which may or may not be accompanied by overt behavior, and that for various reasons a good many persons are arrested at some stage of this evolution. We may find extreme narcissism or homosexual fixation, or frigidity or impotence, or various feelings of guilt associated with masturbation or violation, fancied or actual, of some of the many sexual taboos. This general statement has been the source of much criticism of Freud's psychology, but clinical data certainly appear to bear out its substantial accuracy.

I have indicated earlier that when we find damage to the brain we are likely to find disorders of personality. It should not be thought, however, that all conduct and thinking disorders are dependent upon brain changes. In the present state of our knowledge we consider many of them to be psychologic rather than physiologic in origin, although even Freud expressed the hope that some day we might be able to demonstrate an organic substructure for all of the various mental phenomena.

In addition to the concept of the pervading importance of sex there are two other features of the Freudian psychology, the generally prevailing psychologic doctrine today. One of these is the fact that our conduct, thinking, and perceiving are always colored by emotion, that our feelings affect all of our mental life and behavior. It does not require very attentive listening to some political speeches, for example, to realize that they express almost entirely emotional rather than rational values. Likewise, judgments of persons, of events, of everyday life are colored to a very great extent by what has gone before and that in turn has left its impression because of its emotional value. Some interesting studies have been made upon dispositions of various judges in a given court and wide personal variations have been found which show clearly to how great an extent justice resolves itself into the personality of the judge.[4] Some judges are lenient, some are severe, and two judges of different personalities might dispose of the same case in quite different ways. This is true not only of judges; it is true of everyone. Temperaments are different. Some people are optimists, some are pessimists, some are hypochondriacal, some are suspicious, some trusting, some aggressive, some submissive, and so on. The reasons are not always clear, and indeed very often are not understood even by the person himself. In many instances they could be ascertained by prolonged psychological study. These temperamental differences color all thinking and acting. As Dr. Wilfred Trotter puts it, "All processes of reasoning, however abstract, are participated in and influenced by feeling. We cannot separate off the reasoning process as such and set it to work in an emotional vacuum. There are many emotional states of which the action may be so deeply masked that it is impossible by direct observation to detect them at work, such, for example, as the influence of nationalism, religion, personal vanity and fear, of death, of cruelty, of humiliation. Do not let us cherish the delusion that we can catch these in action and cast them out. We contain them a little, only perhaps to make them more insidious, but even in the most dispassioned train of reasoning they are apt to exercise a steady, treacherous pressure. One may say 'I am looking at it without prejudice.' It is always untrue. We should do well on these occasions to inquire closely by what precise mechanism this supernatural purgation has been effected." [5] We shall advert later to the influence of prejudice and bias, which of course are all emotionally conditioned, upon not only the functioning of the judge and of the attorneys but of the witnesses, and their relation to the dichotomy of "fact" and "conclusion." The very accuracy of one's observation is constantly subject to emotional factors and backgrounds.

It can readily be seen that such an attitude concerning emotion casts a good deal of doubt upon the supremacy of reason, the last stronghold of mankind. Just as

Galileo and Copernicus attacked the concept of geo-
centricity and as Darwin attacked the doctrine of a
special creation, so Freud demonstrated the driving force
of emotion. It is not strange, then, that there has been
resistance to the acceptance of this doctrine. We may
try to be dispassionate. We may, indeed, overcompensate
in that line, but let no one think that he is free of
prejudice. The unbiased man does not exist!

The other objection made to modern psychiatric concepts is that they are deterministic. What does this hated
word "determinism" mean? It means in essence simply
that mental functioning, like physical functioning and
like the functioning of the rest of the universe, is subject to laws, and that to some extent at least it can be
predicted. There are perhaps more unknowns in the
equation, and the cause of any psychologic datum is
never unitary. It is always dependent on a number of
factors which have gone before. The fact of determinism, however, does not mean that man is functioning
blindly. It does not negate the doctrine of free will, that
cherished doctrine of the law. Man is capable, even
though conditioned by what has gone before, of testing
his impulses and desires by reality and making decisions;
indeed, the prospect of penalties for violation of the
prevailing code of conduct is one of the elements of
reality! It is only because there is determinism that
rules of conduct can be expected to have any effect, or
that any sort of treatment for mental disorders can be
helpful. The only alternative to determinism is inde-
terminism with all that that implies of chaos, unpredict-
ability, blind chance, and denial of cause and effect.

Modern psychiatry does not at least in this respect threaten the groundwork of the law by denying the ability of man to make decisions as to his conduct.

At the time when Isaac Ray wrote his volume and for a considerable period of time afterwards (at the time of the Answers in the case of McNaghten, for example) the so-called "faculty psychology" was in force. It was fully believed, not only by Ray, but by other medical writers, such as Pinel, Esquirol, and Prichard, as well as by the legal profession, that a person could have a delusion on one subject and be entirely sane otherwise. There has been much discussion in the past, and is still, of "monomania" and of "partial insanity." In view of what we have just said about the modern views of mental disorder, however, it should be clear that the mind does not function in sections or parts, that except for purposes of description it is unitary in its functioning, and dependent on a vast number of antecedent and concurrent factors. The heredity and the temperament, as well as the physical constitution of the individual, his level of intelligence, his body build, the functioning of his various physical organs, his early and later relations with his parents and siblings, his feelings of security and insecurity engendered by those relations, the other experiences through which he has lived both as a child and as an adult, the "set" of his reactivity, the degree of his extroversion or introversion, the existence of various complexes, all are factors in assessing any given situation in the mental functioning of any individual, whether that functioning be considered normal or pathologic.

The roles of the unconscious and of the emotional drives of the subject are so important while at the same time so hidden or disguised, that to take any one symptom or phase of conduct out of its context may give rise to serious injustices and misunderstandings. If we examine at close range a small section of an oil painting, for example, we see merely a few daubs of color, whereas at a little distance these fall into place as parts of a picture and we wonder how we could have failed before to grasp their significance. This analogy is entirely applicable to any particular aspects of an individual's conduct. Misconception or ignorance of this truth is well illustrated in the technique of attorneys sometimes employed in cross-examination which consists of picking the clinical picture apart and asking if this or that symptom alone justifies the witness's opinion.

The assessment of conduct in any field, then, is a difficult and complicated matter. There is general agreement among psychiatrists upon the essential facts and the significance of words and actions, although there are minor differences in theory. The differences and disagreements are much exaggerated by the critics, and constitute one of the alleged reasons for the reluctance of the legal profession to accept any more readily than they do psychiatric concepts and teachings. Since psychiatry is relatively new as a specialty, they probably account for some of the hesitancy of jurists. In certain students of the law, however, there is more than reluctance. A newspaper dispatch only three years ago, for example, reported that a certain judge in one of our commonwealths declined to have a defendant examined because he considered "all psychiatrists mental defectives," but he did think that he *might* have the defendant examined by a general practitioner! An attitude of the sort just described is, of course, not typical, but is met on occasion.

Some years ago Professor Jerome Michael of Columbia Law School [6] outlined some of the reasons for the skepticism of lawyers as regards psychiatrists as follows: "Psychiatrists, for one, are inclined to make extravagant claims." This is perhaps true of a very small minority, although that minority may be somewhat vocal. Secondly, the "unreliability of their diagnosis." This is a rather inclusive statement. If it means that their diagnoses are unreliable when expressed in terms of the law's concepts, psychiatrists may plead guilty on the ground that they do not speak the language of the law. It is true, also, that psychiatrists do not always agree on the diagnosis of a given case, but given the same set of facts they are likely to come to substantial agreement. He goes on to speak of their "fantastic testimony" and the fact that they disagree. It might be retorted that given the same set of facts lawyers and even judges do not always agree! Dissenting opinions are far from unknown, and certainly if lawyers all agreed there would be precious few contests in court! Professor Michael finally says, "Either those who disagree are not scientists or what they disagree about is not science."

This, of course, goes to the heart of the matter. The psychiatrist does not have before him anything even so tangible as an X-ray picture or gastric analysis or a blood count. At least he may have them, but they are not the basis of his diagnosis. He is dealing with a human being whom he has to see not only in cross-section but longitudinally, a person who has had varied experiences and who has a make-up which is temperamentally, intellectually, and historically unique. Under those circumstances the psychiatrist would be rash if he were to become dogmatic. He can, however, draw certain conclusions, constituting an evaluation of his mental functioning, which should be helpful in the determination of the question at issue.

He is aware that each case has its individual features, depending on the experience and background of the person concerned, that all illness is the product in the last analysis of many factors, and that this is particularly true in the case of personality disorders. Some of the factors are precipitating, some are merely predisposing, others may become perpetuating. The various disorders of behavior and of personality may vary from patient to patient in degree as well as in kind. For these reasons it is extremely difficult for the psychiatrist to categorize, to say with finality that the individual should be placed in a certain pigeonhole. Some cases are so marked that the passer-by may observe them, but there are many which are borderline.

A brief statement concerning the general classification of mental disorders seems to be in order at this point. Obviously a full discussion would involve a course in psychiatry; nevertheless something of the frame of reference of the psychiatrist will perhaps clarify some of the things which we may say further regarding his attitude toward legal concepts. Most of the disorders which we shall mention result in a disturbance of behavior, or at least in a disturbance of the patient's attitude and relations toward himself, or others, or both.

For various reasons, some of them hereditary, but many of them due to intra-uterine accidents or early injuries or infections, the brain may fail to develop. This condition is known as mental deficiency or feeblemindedness. There are several grades, ranging from the idiot who may be even unable to speak or to learn the most elementary needs of toilet function, through the imbecile who has a somewhat higher mental age, to the moron or the person of dull or borderline intelligence. In mental deficiency there is an inability to learn and to exercise the reasoning powers consistently with the patient's chronological age. Judgment is impaired, suggestibility is high, and very frequently there is marked emotional instability, manifesting itself in apparently spontaneous rages and tantrums. Provision may have to be made not only for guardianship but for the commitment to special institutions of such persons, and questions relative to their capacity as witnesses or their responsibility when charged with offenses may arise.

Next there is a group of major mental disturbances generally classified as psychoses (roughly but not accurately synonymous with the "insanities," to use a legal term), in which the disorder is to a large extent physically determined. The most common of these is what is known as delirium, usually due to fever or to some drug intoxication such as from alcohol, bromides, or the barbiturates, or in certain other conditions, such as kidney disease or failing compensation of the heart. In delirium there are disturbances of consciousness ranging from very mild confusion to coma, and disorientation, that is, failure to appreciate properly one's relation to time or place or persons, or all three. The disturbance of consciousness may be of an intermittent nature, in which case the question of "lucid interval" may arise. There may be active hallucinations, very often in the visual field, and transitory delusions. The emotional coloring is likely to be one of fear. The condition in some ways resembles the dream state, and like a dream is likely to be of relatively brief duration, usually subsiding as the intoxication or other physiological disorder abates. Occasionally there are permanent after-effects, such as mental enfeeblement or a psychotic state; the alcoholic, for example, who has delirium tremens may develop a prolonged psychosis, sometimes marked with delusions of persecution, especially directed against the spouse.

Another type in this group of the physically determined disorders is the group in which dementia, that is, loss of reasoning ability (literally "loss of mind"), is a characteristic symptom. The most frequent type of mental disease of this sort is the senile and arteriosclerotic group, in which there is substantial generalized brain damage due to hardening of the arteries, apoplexy (brain hemorrhage), or general senile decay. Some types of diffuse brain damage are due to infections, such as the syphilitic involvement of general paresis, or encephalitis, the so-called "sleeping sickness." Brain damage due to head injury is included in this group. An interesting question may arise as time goes on as to the ultimate effects of the surgical interference known as lobotomy, or leucotomy (the cutting of certain nerve pathways in the brain), now being used to a considerable (probably too great!) extent in the treatment of certain types of mental disease; the bearing of this operation on subsequent disturbances of behavior may well become of legal interest. Brain tumors may cause disturbances in this group, although as a rule the symptoms are in the nature of headache and somnolence, or disturbance of vision.

Characteristic of all of the dementing types of mental disorder is first of all a failure in judgment, with loss of ability to weigh critically the demands of a situation, failing memory, particularly for more recent events, disorientation as a corollary of the memory disturbance, and the development of various defense mechanisms such as delusions, particularly of a persecutory nature. Irritability is increased, the perceptions are dimmed, and often there is a considerable degree of confusion. There is a tendency to shut one's self off from the stream of life and to dwell in the past, with a garrulous tendency to tell about the "good old days." These conditions are of especial interest in connection with questions of testamentary capacity and competency in general. Some male patients of this type may too become involved in sexual advances to small children.

We have spoken of the conditions in which a physical disorder is particularly prominent as the basis, some of these conditions being transitory, but others tending to be permanent and progressive. There is a considerable group of disturbances of personality, however, in which we now consider the causation to be primarily psychologic. This includes the entire group, for example, of what are known as the neuroses or the psychoneuroses. In these conditions, not always distinguished clearly from the psychoses, the patient is aware that he is not well, although he very often does not recognize the nature of his difficulty. He may have numerous physical complaints, or he may instead complain largely of disturbances of thought or feeling. In the obsessional type of neurosis, for example, the patient complains of recurrent ideas or phrases which continually obtrude themselves upon his attention, or he may be full of doubts and questionings whether he has done what he should do, perhaps returning a half-dozen times to see whether he has locked the door as he left the house. He may complain of paroxysmal feelings of vague and unnamed dread, known as anxiety attacks; these are usually accompanied by palpitation, shortness of breath, sweating, and tremulousness. He may have compulsions to do certain repetitive acts (obsessions and tics) or he may find himself driven to resort to large amounts of alcohol or of narcotic drugs. Many cases, at least, of alcoholism and of drug addiction are now thought to be fundamentally neurotic in basis. As for the physical symptoms of neurosis, they are legion. There may be anesthesia (loss of sensation), blindness or deafness, loss of voice (aphonia), or paralysis in what is known as the conversion type of neurosis, formerly referred to as hysteria. There may, too, be tremors, or even attacks of unconsciousness with convulsions. In the conversion neurosis it is usually the sensory or motor systems which are affected. In others of the neuroses the vegetative system is predominantly affected instead, so that we may find painful symptoms referable to almost any system of the body such as the gastro-intestinal tract, the circulatory or genito-urinary system, the skin, and so on. Some of these patients become "surgical addicts," demanding operations for persistent pains for which an organic basis is not found at operation. It is this group which is generally referred to as coming within the domain of psychosomatic medicine. The importance of this group of symptoms in the so-called traumatic neuroses, that is, neuroses which appear at least to have been precipitated by a physical injury, or an emotional shock, is considerable. It should not be thought that merely because the symptom, painful or otherwise, is psychologically determined, it is "imaginary" or "non-existent." The complaints are painfully real; they do not respond well to physical treatment, except so far as that is suggestive therapy, but call for psychologic treatment instead. The same is true of the "reality" of the hallucinations and delusions of the psychotic; if anything, they are to the patient more real than our "reality." Most, too, of these symptoms, especially in the neuroses, are amenable to treatment.

One feature of the neuroses is what is known as "secondary gain." It will usually be found, and not only in the so-called traumatic neuroses, that a useful purpose is served by the symptomatology, whether that be the gaining of sympathy, the evasion of work or other responsibility, or control over another. This mechanism is an unconscious one, but nevertheless potent. The distinction between neurosis and malingering (conscious assumption of symptoms with intent to deceive) lies largely in the degree to which the mechanisms are unconscious and not within the clear awareness of the patient. Even the fact that a patient may improve after an award of damages does not prove malingering. This is said in fairness, although a few cases come dangerously close to the line of conscious exaggeration!

Amnesic states, in which there is a loss of memory sometimes lasting for long periods, are sometimes found in the neuroses, as well as somnambulism. We have now learned, too, that probably most of the cases of so-called sexual perversions, which were formerly known as "sexual psychopathy" and which are the subject of considerable recent legislation, are essentially neurotic, and represent a fixation at an earlier level of psychosexual development.

In addition to this vast group of the neuroses there are certain psychoses which we consider primarily of psychologic origin, though not without their physical components. The largest of these is what is known as schizophrenia or dementia praecox. Much research has been done in recent years, for example, at the Worcester State Hospital, on some of the physical concomitants of this disorder, and it has been found that there are certain physiological inadequacies, notably in the adrenal gland, which may be related to some of the manifestations of this disorder. Fundamentally, the psychologic difficulty in schizophrenia appears to be a regression toward an earlier, less mature mode of

thinking and of feeling, with the development of
magical thinking, the substitution of fantasy for reality,
bizarre interpretations of the surrounding world, delusions and hallucinations, and in some instances panic
and violent action on the one hand or catatonic mutism
and stupor on the other. A moderate, although somewhat decreasing number of patients suffering from
schizophrenia tend to run a progressive course, but the
prognosis is steadily becoming better as our means of
treatment develop.

Delusions, referred to above, are more than merely
false beliefs. The latter are, as a matter of fact, not in
accord with the situation, and the falsity is usually not
demonstrable to the person cherishing the belief, but
delusions have other characteristics as well. A false belief
may be considered delusional if it is one that a person
of similar education and experience would consider im-
probable or impossible, and which is not corrected by
reason or logical demonstration. Even this definition is
not adequate. Actually the delusion is highly colored
by the emotional needs and desires of the individual.
The person who has committed a serious crime, for
example, reads into the casual glances of the passers-by
meanings which do not exist. The basis of the delusion
is sometimes difficult to determine on account of the
disguises which are adopted by the Unconscious, but
they do not exist alone or just happen, since they are
manifestations of a fundamentally disordered emotional
life in the patient. Some of them are highly systematized,
others rather fleeting, and the content varies from patient to patient. The definition of delusions, to the

psychiatrist, is thus far more inclusive than the legal concept of a "belief in things which do not exist, and which no rational mind would believe to exist" (Burris v. Burris, 210 Ky. 731, 276 S.W. 820, 1925). To the psychiatrist, the fact that there are some facts which may be twisted into a delusional system does not by any means exclude the possibility of a delusion. We shall speak more of delusions in discussing testamentary capacity. Hallucinations, as the term is used in modern psychiatric parlance, are disturbances of perception. That is, the patient sees, hears, smells, feels, or tastes something which has no external reality. These again are projections of the inner needs and feelings of the patient. They are to be distinguished from illusions, which are misapprehensions of objects which are actually perceived, and which are normal experiences. Delusions are a very common symptom in many of the mental illnesses. Hallucinations are particularly frequent in the deliria and in the schizophrenic disorders.

Another very common mental disorder probably psychologic in origin is the so-called manic-depressive psychosis. This term is applied because the disturbance has two phases, one (the manic) characterized by emotional elation and overactivity with quickened but disorganized thought processes, and the other the depressive, manifested by feelings of despondency and gloom, with retardation of physical activity, and with slowing of the thought processes. The depressions are about three times as frequent as the manic manifestations, a fact from which a philosopher might derive some comments as to the sadness of human existence! There is also a form of depression which tends to occur in the later periods of life, the so-called involutional psychosis, and which may be accompanied by great physical agitation and restlessness. In all of the depressions thoughts of death and of foreboding are common and suicide is far from uncommon. It is, indeed, always a danger in the depressions. In these so-called "functional" disorders (i.e. those of psychologic origin) the memory is usually not grossly disturbed, although attention, always a factor in memory, may be. The fact, that is, that one can remember well is not necessarily an index of mental soundness.

A special type of mental disorder which has largely a physical basis should be mentioned, namely, the epileptic psychoses. There are various conditions in which the patient suffers from convulsions, with loss of consciousness, or sometimes from attacks of loss of consciousness without the convulsion. The most common type is not fully understood, and for that reason the equivocal adjective "essential" or "idiopathic" is used. The electro-encephalographic tracings are quite characteristic in this disorder. An epileptic may exhibit furors during which he may commit a serious offense, usually highly aggressive in type. These furors are, however, relatively rare compared with the total number of epileptics, and most epileptics are not sufficiently affected mentally to be termed psychotic.

Finally, we should mention what is sometimes referred to as psychopathic personality. This was described by Pinel and by many of the early writers, and was argued at considerable length by Ray in some of his writings. One hundred years ago the disorder was termed by Prichard "moral mania," or "moral insanity," the assumption being that the affective or "moral" aspect of the personality was disturbed without a corresponding disturbance of the reasoning faculties. Later on the term "psychopathic personality" was utilized and for a time at least well merited the appellation of the "waste basket of psychiatry." In recent years, through the studies particularly of Karpman and Maughs, the concept has been very much delimited, and many of the cases which were formerly considered to fall in this group are now considered to be neurotic rather than psychopathic. The psychopathic personality has always been looked upon in the literature as a personality disorder rather than as a psychosis and has in only the rarest instances (those accompanied by acute psychotic episodes) been looked upon as affecting fundamentally the mental accountability of the subject. The latest nomenclature has substituted the term "sociopathic personality disturbance" under the general subheading of personality disorders. A large literature has developed on the subject of psychopathic personality, but for practical purposes very little discussion of it as an entity is called for here.

It should be borne in mind that in all of the types of mental disorder already mentioned it is the sum total of symptoms and history upon which a diagnosis is made. As Ray expressed it succinctly, "Insanity [the word was used then by medical men as equivalent with "psychosis"] is a disease, and as is the case with all other diseases, the fact of its existence is never established by a single diagnostic symptom, but by the whole body of symptoms, no particular one of which is present in every case."

II

SOME DIFFERENCES OF VIEWPOINT

Now that we have considered briefly some of the psychiatric viewpoints with relation to human behavior it may be in order if we proceed to view a few legal practices and assumptions in the light of the data already presented. I have already mentioned the tendency of the law to preserve the status quo, or at least to move slowly in the acceptance of new viewpoints and scientific data. There are judges and lawyers, too, who manifest in extreme form this attitude of *stare decisis,* and emulate Lot's wife in looking backward. This has relation to the tendency of laws to remain on the books after the bases for them have ceased. It may surprise some, for example, to know that the Witchcraft Act of 1735 is still in force in Great Britain and that as recently as 1944 a man was convicted under it of a "pretence to conjuration"! [7] There are numerous instances of laws which have lapsed into desuetude, but these are likely to be repealed eventually (sometimes *much* later!), when public opinion has clearly made them obsolete.

As a sample of this tendency to "view with alarm" any change, one may quote a Pennsylvania court warning that juries "should not indulge in impracticable theories, often subtle and to the ordinary mind incomprehensible, which lead to the acquittal of the guilty and

[39]

to the final destruction of that security which society demands." [8] In a more recent case in New Jersey we find this pearl of wisdom: [After reaffirming the McNaghten Rule] "There are many rules of law which are not perhaps logical. They can from the standpoint of logic be successfully attacked. Yet many of these laws remain unaltered by statute or decision because they have stood the test of practical trial. Our courts are not schools of logic. They administer the law, and the law should not be changed because a case arises in which its application to the facts appears to result oppressively." The court then goes on to make this statement, wholly unwarranted by the statistics of crime: "In every jurisdiction in which the rule that one who consciously commits a crime and knows the difference between right and wrong has been impaired personal security and property rights have suffered." [9] Another example which I have long remembered was that of an elderly judge whom I visited in his chambers one day when he was preparing to charge the jury in a case of bastardy. Since the question of the length of pregnancy was a point at issue he was looking up the matter—in an ancient law dictionary which quoted as authority Lord Coke. It occurred to me at the time that possibly a modern text-book on obstetrics would be more to the point!

Another comment is that the law does not necessarily have anything to do with morals or ethics. The two, at least, are not synonymous, although by and large the law reflects the generally accepted rules of conduct. Sir James Stephen, commenting on this point, says, "Does then the law affirm any, and if so, what system of morals to be true? The law makes no such affirmation. It has nothing whatever to do with truth. It is an exclusively practical system invented and maintained for an actually existing state of society." [10] This occasional non-concurrence of ethics and law is well illustrated by a case recently decided by the Supreme Court of the United States in which it was held that the payment of so-called "kick-backs" to physicians by an optical company was a legitimate business expense. The decision goes on to say, "We voice no approval of the business ethics or public policy involved in the payments now before us. . . . We recognize the organized activities of the medical profession in dealing with the subject," and a footnote adds, "The present trend may lead to the complete abolition of the practice. If so, its abolition will have been accomplished largely by the direct action of those qualified to pass judgment on its justification." [11]

One of the fundamental assumptions of the law, to which we have adverted previously, is that most acts are done on a basis of reasoning and a weighing of the pros and cons. To be sure, there are some exceptions made by the law, such as "heat of blood" and drunkenness. It is well recognized that certain acts are performed under the stress of emotion, such as anger, or that normal inhibitions are otherwise relaxed, and that this emotion militates against premeditation and to some extent at least constitutes a mitigating circumstance. It may operate, for example, to reduce first degree to second degree murder; there are other situations in which the principle is well recognized, though rarely being carried to the extreme to which a psychiatrist might be willing to see it pushed. It is not generally recognized, however, that there are other factors at work in conduct than reason and that there are circumstances under which emotional drives, little understood by the actor, may cause him to perform acts even against his will. There certainly is such a condition as kleptomania, although it will be found in the study of individual cases of this sort that the true kleptomaniac has other symptoms of neurosis as well, thus illustrating again the danger of making a diagnosis by one symptom only. The whole range of offenses which may be committed under the influence of unconscious drives of the impulsive variety has been recognized in the laws of about 19 of the American states (but not at all in England) under the general term of the "irresistible impulse test." It would be of interest to consider at length the question of criminal responsibility, but I have chosen to limit my discussion of this question, in view of the fact that it has been treated at length and most clearly and effectively, by Professor Sheldon Glueck, in his masterly treatise on *Mental Disorder and the Criminal Law.*

Briefly, it may be pointed out that the McNaghten case, in which the so-called right and wrong test was laid down over 100 years ago, was really not a case at all, but a set of questions inspired by a particular case which had already been decided, and in which paranoia was the issue. At that time the so-called "compartment theory" of mental functioning was in vogue, consistently with the then prevalent interest in phrenology. The case was one in which delusions of persecution were a prominent feature, and it was inevitable that the judges had in mind the case of McNaghten himself. The Supreme Court of New Hampshire in commenting upon this case in 1871 stated, "An examination of the answers given shows that they failed utterly to do any such thing" (that is, give a safe, practical legal test) "and it is not too much to say that if they did not make the path to be pursued absolutely more uncertain and more dark they at best shed but little light upon its windings and furnished no plain or safe clue to the labyrinth." That court held that the matter of insanity as a defense was one of fact rather than of law, that the jury should be asked to determine whether or not the act was the offspring or product of mental disease in the defendant. They concluded, "We have consented to receive those facts as developed and ascertained by the researches and observations of our own day instead of adhering blindly to dogmas which were accepted as facts of science and erroneously promulgated as principles of law 50 or 100 years ago." [12] More recently (1952) the dissenting judges in a United States Circuit Court of Appeals case remarked, "The rule of McNaghten's case was created by decision. Perhaps it is not too much to think that it may be altered by the same means." [13]

The outgivings of the judicial mind on the very difficult problem of premeditation, a point on which many men have been executed, are confusing and confused. One of our most thoughtful and learned judges, the late Benjamin Cardozo, in an address before the New York Academy of Medicine in 1928 said, "I think the students of the mind should make it clear to the law-makers that the statute is framed along the lines of a defective and unreal psychology. If intent is deliberate and premeditated whenever there is choice, then in truth it is always deliberate and premeditated, since choice is involved in the hypothesis of the intent. . . . I have no objection to giving them [the jury] this dispensing power, but it should be given to them directly and not in a mystifying cloud of words. The present distinction is so obscure that no jury hearing it for the first time can fairly be expected to assimilate and understand it. I am not at all sure that I understand it myself after trying to apply it for many years and after diligent study of what has been written in the books. Upon the basis of this fine distinction with its obscure and mystifying psychology scores of men have gone to their deaths." [14]

A case decided by a 5-3 decision of the United States Supreme Court (66 S.C. 1318) in 1946 aptly illustrates Justice Cardozo's remarks. The defendant, Fisher, a Negro janitor at the Episcopal Cathedral in Washington, D.C., beat the librarian of the Cathedral to death when he became angered at her chiding and epithets, and he was convicted of first degree murder. The evidence was to the effect that he had reached the third grade of school when he left at 14, that his mental age was $11\frac{4}{12}$ years by tests; that he had been treated for syphilis, and that he had neurologic and serologic evidence suggestive of syphilitic involvement of the brain; that he had long been a heavy drinker, and that on the night before the killing he had been intoxicated. A psychiatrist testified that from his examinations he considered Fisher an "aggressive and impulsive psychopath."

He was, as Mr. Justice Frankfurter summarized it in his vigorous dissent, "a man of primitive emotions reacting to the sudden stimulus of insult and proceeding from that point without purpose or design." Even the prosecution's psychiatrist (who had *not* examined the defendant!) testified that "he was very mad and there was provocation." The majority decision sustained the District Court's refusal to instruct the jury that it might weigh the evidence of the defendant's mental deficiencies in determining the presence or absence of premeditation and deliberation. Mr. Justice Frankfurter was joined by Justices Murphy and Rutledge in dissenting, but Fisher was executed. Professor Keedy, in a scholarly article on the decision, says "When the problem of the Fisher Case again arises a correct solution can be expected if the judges will not try to be amateur psychiatrists but will reason as lawyers, applying the requirements of the statute to the evidence of the particular case." [15]

This case illustrates another related point, namely the law's devotion to the dichotomy between complete "sanity" on the one hand and complete "insanity" on the other, the notion that there are no gradations or shadings. Former Judge Thurman Arnold stated it thus in a decision in 1945: "To the psychiatrist mental cases are a series of imperceptible gradations from the mild psychopath to the extreme psychotic, whereas criminal law allows for no gradations" (Holloway v. U.S., 148 F. 2nd 665). A reference to our earlier consideration of the psychiatric viewpoint will indicate the gulf—a gulf which, however, is gradually being narrowed and

bridged by some newer legislative activities to be discussed later. We may repeat, however, to the physician
that health and sanity are both only relative terms.
There is a wide gamut between the dying invalid and
the professional athlete, somewhere between the two
extremes of which most of us are found. In the same
way the person of superb mental balance and intelligence is far removed from the driveling idiot or the
regressed schizophrenic, completely rapt in his fantasies
and out of contact with the world.

Another aspect of the emotional factors in conduct
has to do with an all too common phenomenon, that of
suicide. In the English law suicide constituted a felony,
felo de se, and the vengeance of the law was wreaked on
the successful victim, as it was on the unsuccessful at-
tempter. In England, suicides were buried at the cross-
roads with a stake through the body, and this practice
was not discontinued by law until 1823. Confiscation of
property, which was applicable to all felonies, including
suicide, was indeed not abandoned until 1870. In England it is still a legal offense, and a British psychiatrist
informs me that about one half of one per cent of the
persons who attempt suicide are imprisoned for times
ranging up to six months. The number is not large,
and the intention is primarily to give protection, but
the basis of considering them offenders rather than
sick is psychiatrically unsound. Fortunately in this country, although the statutes still remain on the books of
some of the states, a more enlightened attitude toward
suicide has been in effect and it is pretty generally recognized by the law, as it is of course by psychiatrists and

by the general public, that the presumption in the case of a suicide or attempted suicide is that the person is suffering from a serious mental disturbance. It cannot be said, perhaps, that *all* suicides are due to mental disorder, but certainly the vast majority of them are. The person who makes an attempt upon his life should certainly have the benefit of psychiatric attention for his own protection before he is released to his own custody, but the idea of proceeding against him as a criminal is a medieval relic.

In the field of legislation we often have an opportunity to see the potent influence of emotion as opposed to reason or as affecting reason and strengthening specious pleas. This is particularly true in legislation having to do with some of the offenses which stir up serious public antipathy and fear. There has been of late, for example, almost an epidemic of "sexual psychopath" laws, so called, which we shall discuss more in detail shortly. The Supreme Court of New Hampshire commented that on this subject there has recently been an extensive amount of literature, popular, scientific, and legal. "Some of it," said the Court, "emits more emotion than enlightenment." [16] Some of the legislation was passed hurriedly before the problems could be adequately studied, spurred on by some one or two dramatic offenses. Occasionally in the past, too, legislators have stooped to epithets in passing legislation. The ancient Massachusetts statute [17] on bestiality, for example, refers to "The abominable and detestable crime against nature"—adjectives not applied to murder, rape, or robbery! Fear or hatred may be very potent factors in

securing the passage of unwise and ill-considered legislation, such, for example, as the notorious whipping-
laws of Delaware and Maryland.

Factors of self-interest are, of course, inescapable, and
now and then we see legislation passed under a fear of
one's own tendency to consider himself unfair or un-
charitable. An example of this sort is the 1952 legislation
in New York which provides that a student may, "con-
sistent with the requirements of public education and
public health," be excused from such study of health
and hygiene as conflicts with the religion of his parents
or guardian. When it comes to forbidding the teaching
of such matters, for example, as the desirability of vac-
cination or the methods by which communicable diseases are transmitted, it would seem that a good deal is
being done in the name of freedom of religion! Certainly a rational basis for this sort of legislation is hard
to see.

Perhaps the best example of public excitement and
demand "to do something" is found in the "sexual
psychopath" legislation, referred to earlier. Although
Michigan passed a law of this sort in 1937 and Illinois
in 1939, up to about the time of the appearance of the
Kinsey Report there were only four states in the whole
country which had legislation of this type, providing
in essence for the indeterminate segregation of certain
persons who are denominated as "sexual psychopaths"
and who presumably are persistent offenders by reason
of mental deviation which in severity falls short of the
legal standards of "insanity." A recent editorial in the
American Journal of Psychiatry (108:629) comments

that this increase in public concern suggests that the wave of sex crimes is mostly an "apparition produced by a wave of public distress and offended dignity." As a matter of fact, criminal statistics have consistently shown no marked increase in sex crimes, although the popular magazine articles about sex problems increased from 16 in number in 1946 to 46 in 1950. A bogey has been raised which paints the mentally abnormal sexual offender as being one who proceeds from trivial offenses such as exhibitionism to serious ones such as rape and murder. Since the so-called "minor" sexual offenses have called for only very short penal confinements, provision has been devised whereby offenders of this sort who were thought to be recidivistic in type could be segregated for an indeterminate period, much as the mentally ill are committed.

Those who have studied the problem agree that a measurable proportion of these offenders are likely to be persistent, although as a matter of fact they usually do not shift their type of offense, and a considerable proportion of them have largely a nuisance value.[18] Many of them are very mild and submissive, and there is but little to indicate that the allegations which have brought about the passage of this legislation are in line with the facts.

Nevertheless, the "sexual psychopath" legislation is significant and has hit upon a truth almost unknowingly. Many of the persistent sexual offenders, notably those who engage in so-called paraphilic ("perverted") practices such as homosexuality or exhibitionism or who make sexual advances to young children of either sex, are mentally abnormal, the bulk of them probably suffering from a neurotic fixation. Furthermore, a measurable share of them are amenable to treatment. For this reason the procedure should be different from the present method of sentencing the general run of prisoners. The significant feature pointing toward the future is the fact that here is a recognition by the law that there are persons who stand between the shade of "insanity" and the sunlight of sanity, that there is a middle ground which calls for special handling and for an indeterminate period of segregation, during which treatment can be attempted, or who, treatment failing, may be continued in confinement. Legislation of this type is another pointer along the road to the realization of the treatment tribunal, advocated long ago by Professor Glueck and more recently exemplified in the adoption in five states of the Youth Authority recommended by the American Law Institute.[19] California has gone even one step farther by establishing a similar Adult Authority. The day of predetermined fixed sentences à la Beccaria, or indeed the setting of a term of imprisonment by the judge, appears to be drawing to a close, to be succeeded by a true individualization of correctional and penal treatment based largely upon social and psychiatric considerations.

Bowman and Rose, in a thoughtful article in the *American Journal of Psychiatry* for September 1952 (109:177), point out that the term "sexual psychopath" has no clear psychiatric significance, but is merely a convenient label for administrative purposes, social maladjustment in the sexual sphere being the main criterion for applicability. Probably "mentally deviated sex offender" is sounder terminology. Practically all the "sexual psychopath" laws as they now stand (except for Pennsylvania and New York, which have broader provisions) are ineffective administratively; in the District of Columbia, for instance, for the year ending June 30, 1952, just three persons were committed under the "Miller Act," whereas the number of sex offenses showed no decrease! Some years ago I ventured to suggest that if progress is to be made in this or indeed any other criminal field, we should have truly indeterminate sentences, with adequate court clinics and with psychiatric services in correctional institutions, rather than joining "the hue and cry for new laws" (*Mental Hygiene,* 22:20, January 1938).[20]

The recently accentuated public interest in sexual offenses raises some serious questions about the nature of testimony accepted in convicting persons accused of such crimes. Lord Hale, nearly 300 years ago, in speaking of rape said, "It is an accusation easily to be made and hard to be proved and harder to be defended by the party accused, though never so innocent . . . wherein the court and jury may with so much ease be imposed upon without great care and vigilance." [21] More recently a Nebraska court paraphrased the same sentiment thus: "Public sentiment seems inclined to believe a man guilty of any illicit sexual offense he may be charged with." [22] This readiness on the part of the public to believe such charges has some interesting psychological roots in the unconscious strivings of the average citizen, but whatever the explanation, the fact remains. It was dangerous enough at any time but now, particularly in those states with "sexual psychopath" laws in which a man may conceivably be confined for the rest of his life for an offense far less serious than attempt to commit rape, for example, it becomes increasingly important to look carefully to the psychologic bases of some of the evidence. In a recent Indiana case a man was convicted of rape on the unsupported evidence of the prosecuting witness, a 12-year-old girl with an extremely poor background who had reached only grade 4-B. On appeal an affidavit signed by the girl in which she repudiated her earlier testimony (she stated that her original complaint had been made under threats by the police that she would be returned to the reform school if she refused) was presented to the supreme court of the state but was not considered, on the entirely legalistic ground that it was not contained in the special bill of exceptions! [23] For that reason the motion for a new trial was dismissed by the court. Dr. Leo Orenstein, a psychiatrist of long experience in the New York City Court of General Sessions, has recently cited three case histories which are little short of shocking as miscarriages of justice.[24] In one of these, for example, the man was accused by his 12-year-old daughter of having raped her. There was no corroboration, and indeed the physical examination failed to substantiate her charges. Nevertheless so afraid was he of what the result might be if he faced a trial that he pleaded guilty to a minor charge instead, although he knew himself to be innocent. It was subsequently admitted by the complaining witness that her accusations were baseless, but were made out of fear of what her father might do to her when he discovered that she had been having sexual relations with a boy slightly older than herself. A careful investigation by the District Attorney would have indicated that there was at least serious doubt of the truth of the girl's story. In the *Saturday Evening Post* for August 9, 1952 appears the account of a trial in Washington, D.C. with the details of which I am personally familiar. In this instance a highly respected member of the community was accused, on a false identification, of indecent exposure, the accusers being two teen-age girls. They were apparently "well briefed" by the police, and once having made the identification evidently did not dare to alter it. In proceedings which cast no glory whatever upon the fairness or perspicacity of either the prosecuting attorney or the judge the man was found guilty, and had it not been for the fact that the guilty person, a much younger man who bore almost no physical resemblance to the accused, confessed spontaneously when assured that he would not be prosecuted, the accused man would have served a sentence and his reputation would have been ruined.

The fact of the matter is that false accusations of sex offenses may be made not only by honest mistake of identification but deliberately for purposes of blackmail or revenge, as the result of fantasy on the part of the accuser, or even as a symptom of frank psychosis. There is a sound psychologic reason for the general rule of evidence that in a civil or criminal case involving a wrong by a man to a woman's chastity or analogous thereto, the complainant woman's testimony alone, uncorroborated by other evidence, is not sufficient. In the case of child complainants this rule appears to be occasionally forgotten! Many of these accusations are made with lurid details, attract much public attention, and sometimes furnish a good deal of transient glory(?) for the prosecuting officer. It is further a fact that in some of these cases the personality disturbance which lies at the basis of the accusation would not be discernible to laymen, but that the psychiatrist can in many cases give a definite opinion as to the witness's mental state after he has made an examination. Some courts have clinics to which a doubtful case of this sort could be referred, and in the absence of such a clinic the court could appoint experts. It was Dean Wigmore's view, concurred in by a committee of the American Bar Association, that in all cases charging sex offenses, the complaining witness should be examined before the trial by competent psychiatrists as to her (or his) probable credibility. This attitude is confirmed by all psychiatrists who have had experience in this field; outstanding examples are William Healy, the late William Alanson White, and Karl Menninger.[25] There is no doubt that, as Wigmore says, many innocent men have gone to prison "because of tales whose falsity could not be exposed." The jury's decision in such a case is all too likely to be emotionally conditioned, with the odds heavily against the accused.

As a further example of the irrational and emotional reaction caused by rumors of illicit and socially reprobated sexual activity may be mentioned the wholesale accusations and innuendoes which have been leveled at certain groups of government employees of late. Some of the psychologic bases of this modern "jehad" are ably discussed by Karpman in the recent article referred to earlier.

The question of the effect of the witness's mental state upon the credibility of his testimony may arise in cases other than those involving sexual offenses. This was emphasized to the public recently in the second trial of Alger Hiss. During that trial a psychiatrist was asked a 78-minute hypothetical question concerning the credibility of the principal prosecuting witness based upon the latter's alleged history and conduct. The physician, who had not personally examined the witness, was permitted by the judge to answer that in his opinion the hypothetical individual exhibited a "psychopathic personality." Apparently the jury chose to believe the prosecuting witness, despite the diagnosis *à distance*. The objections in this particular case were two, one that although the witness was present in the courtroom the psychiatrist made a diagnosis without a personal examination, and second that the concept of psychopathic personality is at least in a state of flux among psychiatrists. Dr. Philip Q. Roche of Philadelphia has commented in an article that perhaps the "psychopathic personality" is the "heretic" or "witch" in modern guise! [26]

It is not a fact that the Hiss case was the first in which questions of this sort have come up, although the daily papers certainly gave that impression. In one habeas corpus case in 1945, for example, it was held that the fact that a diagnosis of psychopathic personality had been made upon the appellant, then confined in a mental hospital, was rightly taken into consideration in appraising his testimony.[27] In an Illinois arson case, tried in 1930,[28] the sole prosecuting witness, 42 years old, who was also an accomplice, had a mental age of about 9, and had been examined by three physicians, one appointed by the state, one by the defense, and one by the court; all agreed on his mental state. The principal defendant was convicted nevertheless. The conviction was later reversed. A similar Texas case in 1920 [29] involving robbery had the same result. These cases illustrate the psychiatric view that the general rule concerning the disqualification of witnesses by reason of insanity or other form of mental derangement does not go quite so far as it properly might. It may be added that in a study of some of the rules of evidence made by Professor Steuart Henderson Britt [30] all of the psychologists and the lawyers except the professors of evidence themselves question the advisability of the rule as it stands.

The fact is that practically every statement which anyone makes, no matter how factual he may think it, involves a certain amount of conclusion, and every conclusion is to some extent colored by emotion. It is not true, for example, that as a Georgia court recently said, "Where a witness testifies as to what he observes, hears, or smells it is not a conclusion." [31] The fact was much more soundly stated by the North Dakota Supreme Court in an equally recent case as follows: "Where a witness gives the results of what he saw, his testimony is not objectionable on the ground that it is a conclusion rather than a statement of fact. Every result of the use of the eyesight is as a matter of last analysis a deduction or judgment. All evidence, after all, is opinion unless we call it fact and knowledge as discovered and manifested to the observation of the witness." [32] The mental state of the witness, therefore, no matter how hard he tries to tell the truth, is of interest to the court, and sometimes calls for expert advice and diagnosis. The important thing is that such expert advice should be based upon a thorough knowledge of the history of the witness and upon a personal examination. The inaccuracy of observation and of memory exhibited by witnesses even of the best intentions have been discussed by many writers, notably by the late Professor Hugo Munsterberg in his significant volume *On the Witness Stand* (1908). The unreliability of so-called "eye-witness identifications" has been all too often demonstrated; the Sacco-Vanzetti case of Massachusetts, of unhappy memory, bears study in this regard.

Emotionality and mental state also affect jurors as well as witnesses. Much, indeed, might be said and many instances might be cited in which the emotional attitude of the jury more than discounted all of the facts laid before them. This might be sympathy, involving an acquittal in spite of data, or it might be a conviction when the facts were quite clear as to the deranged mental state of the defendant. In Colorado, for example, where ever since 1927 commitment to a mental hospital has been required in the case of any defendant in whose case insanity has been pleaded, a case arose in 1938, when a young man of low intelligence, a former inmate of a school for the feeble-minded, was convicted in spite of an unequivocal report of the doctors that he was incapable of distinguishing between right and wrong. In this case the jury chose to believe the police officers instead of the doctors. Not only was the defendant convicted of murder in the first degree, but the conviction was sustained by the Supreme Court and even the Governor did not interfere with the execution.[33] In another slightly earlier Colorado case a similar conviction took place, but in this case, more happily, the Supreme Court of the state reversed the conviction, that of an old-time schizophrenic of 25 years' standing, with the statement, "The verdict is incomprehensible save upon the supposition that the brutal character of the killing so aroused the passion and prejudice of the jurors as to cause them to overlook or disregard the court's instruction." [34] Again, in a recent case in Massachusetts, where the report not only of the Briggs Law examiners but of the staff of the hospital for the criminal insane where the defendant had been examined, reported that the defendant was mentally ill and insane and where the District Attorney did not present any evidence to the contrary, the jury convicted. In this case, too, the Supreme Judicial Court reversed the judgment and ordered a new trial. The Court commented, "There was no medical testimony that he was responsible. The fact that most men are sane, and a rational probability that the defendant too may have been sane on February 21, 1948 notwithstanding what he then did and later said about it seem to us inadequate reasons upon which to disregard this unanimous medical opinion that he was not." [35] A recent editorial in the *London Times* (August 30, 1952) calls attention to a disturbing English case which has caused "great general anxiety," namely that of Regina v. John Thomas Straffen. A young man, 22 years old, an offender and a certified mental defective since the age of 10, a former inmate of a school for mental defectives but returned to the community when he reached the age of 16, was committed to Broadmoor in October 1951 as mentally "unfit to plead" when arraigned for the strangling of two little girls. Escaping in April 1952 and charged with a third strangling, he was not only found fit to plead, despite evidence that there he had shown little mental change, but convicted of murder and sentenced to be hanged. The Court of Criminal Appeal confirmed the verdict, but fortunately the Home Secretary, who apparently is expected to correct the bungling due to strict interpretation of the McNaghten Rules, has recommended a reprieve. The *Times* comments that the case "has brought out sufficient evidence to satisfy the public that action . . . is required. There should be a drastic overhaul of the criminal laws of insanity." Whether the self-satisfaction of those jurors who play bridge was a factor in the verdict of sound mind can only be guessed; it was testified that Straffen had learned to play contract bridge while at Broadmoor! Or were they actuated only by a fear that return to Broadmoor would not suffice, and that a mentally defective killer must be put out of the way in order that the public might be safe? In any event some significant evidence was disregarded in making obeisance to shades of the McNaghten judges and their century-old rules!

Cases of this sort, criminal and civil alike, could be multiplied indefinitely; they all merely go to show that juries, being composed of men and women subject to human frailties, are often governed by emotions rather than reason. We should perhaps not be too astonished, too, that juries are occasionally misled when subjected to emotional outbursts and psychologic pontifications on the part of the judge. In an Oklahoma murder case, for example, the appellate court was evidently much shocked by some of the history of the defendant in a murder case. Speaking of some of the more lurid parts of the sex history of the defendant the Supreme Court of the state said, "They are just evidence of a looseness of morals that has been encouraged and cultivated by living with prostitutes, whore-mongers, and pimps in houses of ill fame. The details of wickedness related by the defendant were so debased as to startle any rational, moral citizen." [36] Needless to say the verdict was allowed to stand! Or again in a federal court the judge charged in a narcotics case, "You may have noticed . . . that he wiped his hands during the testimony. It is rather a curious thing, but that is almost always an indication of lying. Why it should be so we don't know, but that is a fact. I think that every word that man said *except when he agreed with the Government's testimony* [italics supplied] was a lie." [37] In this instance the Supreme Court reversed the verdict on the ground that the lower court judge had assumed the role of a witness, had distorted the evidence, and had added to it.

To my mind, though, the gem of all charges on the defense of insanity is found in a lower court in Mississippi as follows: "The only absolute defense of insanity known in the State of Mississippi is paranoia. That is just real flat insanity, not temporary. So if you are pleading insanity the only insanity I recognize is paranoia. That is real insanity, not just a lapse of memory or just a sudden forgetting of everything, just real insanity known as paranoia in the medical profession." [38] It is perhaps superfluous to add that this conviction too was reversed on appeal! If we find such misunderstanding on the part of the judiciary perhaps we may be surprised that what appears to the psychiatrist to be justice is done so often as it is!

Another complication is that the law regarding mental disorder and insanity is largely statutory, and that the term "insanity" varies widely in its application. It may also be mentioned, in repetition, that the term is entirely a legal one, which is not used by physicians except on those relatively rare occasions when they have to answer questions about it in court. There are at least five meanings of the word "insane" or "insanity" in legal issues: (1) the lack of capacity to make a valid contract or deed; (2) lack of testamentary capacity, the ability to make a valid will; (3) the degree and type of "insanity" required to nullify capacity to commit crime; (4) fitness for commitment to a mental hospital; (5) incompetency, that is, suitability for guardianship. Thus, depending on the pertinent statute, a variety of issues of fact can be the subject of litigation. [39]

Let us consider for a few moments some of the points

of view regarding testamentary capacity. The law very wisely recognizes that under certain situations involving physical weakness, prolonged illness, or advanced age, a prospective testator's resistance to blandishments or misrepresentations may be lowered to such an extent that he is not to be considered a free agent and that the product of his testamentary activities should not be considered a valid will. He may be taken in by a pretty nurse or by an unscrupulous relative or friend or even, possibly (perish the thought!), by his lawyer, his banker, or his physician. The proof is difficult, and its criteria should be rigorous, since obviously the person who has made the will is never about to say what he means when the will is presented for probate. It is when the question of general incompetency or lack of capacity by reason of a particular delusion comes up that the law is out of line with what the psychiatrist would consider to be the truth of the situation. In the formation of delusions belief is fundamental, and as with normal and socially acceptable beliefs it is true that it is not always to be settled by argument, as witness beliefs in religious or political matters. Interpretation always enters, and since interpretation rests on personal needs, logical reasoning may not be followed. Delusions often are derived from misinterpretation of actual events or they may be, so to speak, spun out of the whole cloth of imagination as ideas or imaginary sensory experience. The former we refer to as delusions, the latter as hallucinations.

Many years ago an eminent British psychiatrist, Charles Mercier (*Criminal Responsibility,* Oxford 1905), speaking of delusions, said, "A delusion is not an isolated disorder. It is merely the superficial indication of a deep-seated and widespread disorder. As a small island is but the summit of an immense mountain rising from the floor of the sea, the portion of the mountain in sight bearing but an insignificant ratio to the mass whose summit it is, so a delusion is merely the conspicuous part of a mental disease, extending, it may be, to the very foundations of the mind, but the greater portion of which is not apparent without careful sounding." The old concept of "monomania," in which a delusion is found without other mental involvement, is not today accepted by psychiatrists, although the word and concept seem to die hard in the law! Delusions may be defense reactions, avoidances, compensations, or projections; they differ in the obviousness of their meaning to the extent that the ego has deteriorated. In terminal states, where the personality has greatly dilapidated, they may stand very frankly for what they are, with relatively little attempt at disguise.

It is only in the most dilapidated psychotic that a delusion is not based to some extent on actual events. Indeed, in the victim of true paranoia we find delusions, fixed suspicions, or grandiose trends which are logically elaborated and with due regard for reality after once a false misinterpretation or premise has been accepted. Such a person may be expected to show excellent memory, formally correct conduct, and clear and coherent thought. This is one reason, of course, why so few paranoiacs are committed to mental hospitals or once committed are detained—in other words, why so many of them are at large!

The question of delusion comes up often in connection with wills, particularly those made by older persons, persons who are often afflicted with sensory difficulties, notably deafness, who are physically ill, whose memory is poor, and who have, in short, numerous handicaps. It is not strange then that they misinterpret, yet the courts are extremely reluctant to disallow a will unless it is shown very clearly and obviously that the provisions of the will were controlled by the delusion. The books are full of cases in which the wills of persons who, to the psychiatrist, were notably out of contact with reality, seriously ill mentally, and deluded, were sustained. For example a Missouri court says, "There is no such thing as a delusion founded on fact," [40] a statement with which the psychiatrist would certainly disagree. Again, a California court states, "One cannot be said to act under a monomania [*sic!*] if his condition results from a belief or inference, however irrational or unfounded, which is drawn from facts which are shown to exist. The essential element of an insane delusion is that it is created without reason or evidence and is adhered to against reason and evidence." [41] In a recent Wisconsin case a man who died at 82 and had made his will five years earlier, changing it twice before his death, thought that his nephew and his wife were stealing things from him. Actually he saw them placing the things in their car but they claimed they were gifts. The court held that there was some basis for the belief and hence that it was not an insane delusion.[42] Actually, such a belief in elderly patients may well, and often does, constitute a delusion. Very often their memory is greatly at fault, and they may even forget that they have given the articles away, or they may believe that articles have been stolen rather than merely misplaced and then forgotten. Nevertheless, from a psychiatric point of view these beliefs are controlling, and constitute delusion. In an Illinois case a contest arose because the deceased had changed the beneficiary of his insurance. He had developed the idea that his wife was unfaithful and was trying to poison him. The court held that there was some evidence, "however slight," and that therefore the deceased's ideas against his wife were not delusions.[43] The comment in the *Oregon Law Review* was to the effect that the courts in this regard had been "in a state of suspended animation since the case of Dew v. Clark in 1826." [44] Actually this statement is not entirely fair, for in the case of Waring v. Waring in 1848 Lord Brougham laid down a principle which seems strikingly modern as we read it today. He said: "The mind is one and indivisible, and if the mind is unsound on one subject it is erroneous to suppose that such a mind is really sound on other subjects. It is only sound in appearance. The frame of mind which indicates the inability of the deceased to struggle against an erroneous belief such as a delusion constitutes an unsound frame of mind." [45] Unfortunately for progress, this case was overruled in Banks v. Goodfellow in 1870, which adopted the compartment theory in these words, "Everyone must be conscious that the faculties and functions of the mind are various and distinct as are the powers and functions of our physical organization." [46] There was, then, a short period of resuscitation from the "state of suspended animation" to which the *Oregon Law Review* article refers.

In the matter of what the law would term "general insanity" the courts have not been very much more in line with psychiatric progress. In a New Jersey case a petition (for a writ de lunatico inquirendo) alleged filthiness in appearance, loss of interest in music, refusal to have a rupture cared for, and stated further that the deceased arose at night and waited to be fed by his deceased wife. Nevertheless it was held that these facts all failed to establish such incompetence so as to warrant the issuance of a commission for inquiry into sanity. The court added, "To warrant finding a man a lunatic, evidence of unsoundness of mind must be such as to import a total deprivation or suspension of the ordinary powers of his mind." [47] Another case in Pennsylvania dealt with a man who died at the age of 89, nine years after he had executed his will, having made several codicils in the interval but no material change. It was testified that he was forgetful, that he lived in poverty and filth, that he was subject to rages and tantrums, and that he refused medical attention. These facts were held not sufficient to prove an unsound mind. The deceased left his money to agnostic societies, which, of course, is not necessarily evidence of mental disease. The court commented "A man's prejudices are part of his liberty," and allowed the probate of the will.[48]

In probate as in criminal law the "all or none" rule is psychiatrically unsound. There are many degrees of paranoia, various shadings of beliefs from the honest mistake to the fantastic delusion. The courts find themselves able to decide whether a certain set of facts constitutes negligence, whether an agent was in the scope of his employment, and to interpret many other similar sets of circumstances in relation to legal rules. In the same way they should not evade by oversimplification their duty to interpret whether certain, possibly delusional, beliefs of a testator which may have influenced him were psychiatrically unsound or whether they were within the bounds of normality. I urge further attention to the application of modern and thoroughly accepted psychiatric knowledge to the law of wills.

To turn to another field, namely that of tort law, a few comments may be made concerning the psychiatric as compared with the legal point of view. In recent years particularly the courts have come to recognize the fact that serious damage of a neurotic nature may be done to an individual, or at least precipitated, by what is generally referred to as "emotional shock." The number of cases of this sort, particularly following automobile accidents, is steadily increasing, and some very substantial verdicts have been given. As a matter of fact, although a neurosis may be precipitated by an emotional shock it is usually in a person who is unduly susceptible to disturbances of this sort. The shock is not the whole cause, but since it is the precipitating factor the element of damage must be considered by the jury. The complaints, which may be of a physical nature such as paralysis, or anesthesia, mutism, hysterical blindness, and so on, or more in the psychologic sphere such as insomnia, bad dreams, and attacks of anxiety, are genuine, in spite of the fact that they have no demonstrable physical basis. There is no need, therefore, for the jury to assume that the symptoms are malingered, although malingering—that is, the conscious assumption or exaggeration of symptoms for gain or other purpose—cannot be excluded in view of the possible considerable pecuniary advantages to be gained. The factor which is often overlooked by juries and needless to say is not usually stressed by the plaintiff's attorney at least, is that the symptoms, disabling and sympathy-provoking though they may be, are not necessarily permanent. Many of the verdicts which have been given seem to indicate an expectation on the part of the jury that the individual would be incapacitated for life, only to find that soon after the verdict was rendered the symptoms largely disappeared. A very striking case of this nature, that of the so-called "Sweet Singer of the South," who recovered completely from hysterical paralysis after a $40,000 settlement, has been cited by Professor Hubert Winston Smith.[49] It is sometimes assumed that the fact that the symptoms disappear after settlement indicates that they were consciously assumed. This does not necessarily follow. The anxiety and worry over possible future earning capacity may operate to maintain symptoms of this sort, and the solution of the problem may by relieving these anxieties produce an amelioration of the symptoms or even recovery. Furthermore, symptoms of this sort, like other neurotic symptoms, are amenable to treatment. It is largely a question of providing sufficient incentive to the patient to wish to give up his symptoms, since as we have seen before, secondary gain is one of the characteristics of all of the neuroses. It may be added that there is much to be said in favor of lump sum settlements in such cases. Situations which make the continuance of monetary gain dependent upon continuation of neurotic symptoms, whether those be due to peace time or war time disabilities, tend, unconsciously to the patient, to perpetuate the illness.

Over 300 years ago, Sir Thomas Browne, one of England's best-loved physicians, in the introduction of his extraordinary volume entitled *Pseudodoxia Epidemica, or Enquiries into very many received Tenents and commonly presumed Truths,* wrote: "Nor have we indeed scarce named any author whose name we doe not honour; and if detraction could invite us, discretion surely would contain us from any derogatory intention, where highest Pens and friendliest Eloquence must fail in commendation."

It is my hope that in outlining some of these differences in point of view I have not appeared carping or overcritical, but that I have tried to emulate Sir Thomas. It is certainly not my intention to carp, even though it is only by criticism and suggestion and by difference of opinion that progress can be brought about. The law, within modest limits, does tend, as the late Justice Oliver Wendell Holmes pointed out in his lectures on The Common Law, to "conform our standards to experience," and much is being done today in the education of law and medical students to bring about a closer understanding. By bringing about such understanding the schools which are now training the future lawyers and physicians of this country will do much to narrow the grounds of criticism and bring about a closer rapprochement of law and medicine.

III

THE MENTAL PATIENT AND
THE HOSPITAL

During 1949 (the latest year for which complete Public Health Service statistics are available), 248,407 persons were admitted to mental hospitals of all types in the United States. During the same period, 184,366, or 74 per cent of that number, were discharged, and at the end of the year there remained nearly 565,000. The annual cost of operating the public institutions of this sort is about 350 million dollars, and if any estimate could be made concerning the loss in earning power of the patients therein, it would probably be not far from one billion dollars! These few figures serve to indicate the economic and social importance of that portion of the mentally ill population of the country whose disorder is sufficiently disabling to lead them to the hospital.

There are several features which distinguish the population of the mental hospital from that of the general hospital. First of all, most of the former, or at least of those caring for about 98 per cent of all of the mentally ill of the country, are operated either by the state or the federal government, the federal hospitals being devoted principally to the care of veterans. Although some of the patients go to the hospital voluntarily, recognizing that they are ill, a very substantial majority of them, lacking in insight, have to be hospitalized without their consent. It is for these reasons that laws have been enacted, providing for the establishment, operation, and supervision of mental hospitals and for the care and detention of those patients who require such care.

The evolution of the mental hospitals has been a long and tortuous one, with many fluctuations in the degree of public interest and in the attitude of the public toward mental patients and mental disease in general.[50] In the colonial days, it was only the "furiously mad" for whom any sort of legal provision was made. At first, in Massachusetts for example, under a statute passed in 1797, authority was given to the judges to commit any person who was "Lunatic and so furiously mad as to render it dangerous to the peace or the safety of the good people for such lunatic to go at large," to the house of correction, there to be detained "until he or she be restored to his right mind." It is interesting that this provision was enacted in the form of an amendment to an Act for Suppressing Rogues, Vagabonds, Common Beggars, and other Idle, Disorderly and Lewd Persons.[51] Even when the State Hospital at Worcester was opened in 1833, it was still only the "furiously mad" and the "manifestly dangerous" who were committed there, and authority was given to the trustees to discharge persons if they were not dangerous or if they were not susceptible of mental improvement by remedial treatment at the hospital. Only a little over 100 years ago (1842), the county commissioners were authorized to provide at the houses of correction "a suitable apartment for idiots and lunatic and insane persons not furiously mad." It was, indeed, her experience in visiting the house of correction in East Cambridge which started Dorothea Lynde Dix on her very effective and wide-ranging crusade on behalf of the mentally ill.

Isaac Ray, in whose memory these lectures are given, dealt to a very substantial extent in his writings with the confinement of the mentally ill. In 1869, he stated as clearly as anyone has ever stated the proper aims of a law relative to the confinement of such patients. Said he: "In the first place, the law should put no hindrance in the way to the prompt use of those instrumentalities which are regarded as most effectual in promoting the comfort and restoration of the patient. Secondly, it should spare all unnecessary exposure of private troubles and all unnecessary conflict with popular prejudices. Thirdly, it should protect individuals from wrongful imprisonment. It would be objection enough to any legal provision that it failed to secure these objects in the completest possible manner." [52] At the time that Ray wrote these words, attention had been focused upon the matter of commitments by some interesting developments in the state of Illinois. Up to 1865 or thereabouts, it was the general rule that except for the "furiously mad," who were subject to court action, admission to mental hospitals, public or private, was a relatively informal process, much as today is admission to a general hospital. It was assumed that if the patient was not able to speak for himself, the family were taking proper interest in his welfare and were arranging for him to be cared for where he could receive the best attention, in accordance with the principles and knowledge of the time. In 1864, one Mrs. Packard, who had spent three years in the state mental hospital at Jacksonville, Illinois, secured her release on a writ of habeas corpus and shortly thereafter began a campaign devoted to the thesis that not only had she but many others been committed and detained, though mentally well. To her, the only proper preventive of such happenings was the trial by jury of any person whose commitment to a mental hospital was proposed. Mrs. Packard secured the passage of a bill in Illinois (1867) and in Iowa (1872), requiring jury trials for commitment, and the agitation which she started spread to a number of other states. In addition, commissions were set up in some of the states for a closer supervision of the mental institutions. A perusal of Mrs. Packard's book, entitled *Modern Persecution, or Insane Asylums Unveiled,* [53] strongly suggests that the author was not entirely well mentally when she was released, but she had the drive and the vigor which sometimes produce startling legislative results. As a matter of fact, Mrs. Packard had been sent to the hospital by her husband under a law then in effect which permitted a husband to confine his wife in a mental hospital if he thought her deranged—he was quite literally the lord and master!

The reaction which Mrs. Packard brought about was so extreme as to be almost calamitous and certainly unfair to the many patients who later on suffered at the hands of juries by the public exhibition of their illness. Dr. Richard Dewey, who was familiar with the entire history of the case, wrote, many years later, "The entire annals of the insane in the state of Illinois furnish no greater evidence of cruelty to the insane and their friends than this so-called 'reform,' so zealously promoted by Mrs. Packard. As a matter of fact, more persons were found insane by jury trials . . . than were ever wrongfully committed under the earlier system. The effect upon the patient was frequently detrimental, arousing in his mind the idea that the court proceedings were for the purpose of substantiating some charge against him, and when found insane he believed himself innocently condemned." [54]

Fortunately, nearly all of the mandatory jury trials have finally been wiped off the books. Indeed, aside from the Territory of Alaska, the only part of the United States where jury trial is mandatory is the state of Texas; there, persons detained in hospital for more than 90 days must appear before a jury. Although many states have made their procedures less objectionable, there is much room for improvement. In 1950, the Federal Security Agency took the initiative in improving procedures by proposing to the several states a draft act governing the hospitalization of the mentally ill; already at least two states have enacted the proposal, and several others are considering the possibility of doing so. Improvement in this field, too, was one of the recommendations made to the Governors' Conference by the Council of State Governments in a significant report on *The Mental Health Programs of the 48 States,* published in 1950.

When the ordinary individual becomes ill with some surgical or medical condition, he is likely to recognize the fact that he is ill and to seek help, if necessary going voluntarily to a hospital when so advised. In the case of the mentally ill person, particularly if he has no startling concomitant physical complaints, he may fail to realize that he is ill and may, indeed, not believe his physician or his family if he is told that he is sick. He is likely, too, to have some inaccurate and twisted ideas about mental hospitals and mental disease in general and to think of the latter as bearing the same stigma as criminality.

Presumably hospitals exist for the care of the ill, and therefore it seems only proper that medical authorities should be the ones to deal with the admission of patients to such hospitals. On the other hand, if a patient is not willing to submit himself to needed hospital treatment, the question of his involuntary detention arises; that immediately raises questions as to his civil rights. For this reason, commitment has been handled largely by the courts or by judges in their magisterial capacity, as in Massachusetts, or by commissions of some sort with a distinctly legal flavor. All too often the procedure savors much of the criminal. In the New Mexico law,[55] for instance, the alleged insane person is "apprehended" on a "warrant" delivered to some peace officer, is notified that he is being "charged with insanity," and is given a "hearing" on such a "charge"; he is then "arraigned" on this charge, to which he may offer a "defense." He must be present at this hearing, whether he knows what is going on or not; finally he is conveyed to the "insane asylum" by the sheriff!

In many states the patient is detained in jail pending the proceedings, so that it is not strange that when he reaches the hospital he fancies that he is undergoing punishment in a correctional or penal institution, thus confirming any feelings of guilt he may have. In over 20 states he may, if he objects to being sent to the hospital, demand that he be tried by a jury—the jury, of course, having little or no knowledge concerning mental hospitals or mental disease and almost as likely as not to commit the wrong person or to set free a dangerous one. There seems little doubt, too, that highly formalized proceedings tend to cause the family to postpone attempting to secure hospital care for the patient, partly out of feeling for the patient and partly out of fear of damage to their own pride and self-esteem. In the District of Columbia, for example, formal notice of hearing is served on the prospective patient, witnesses are summoned, and testimony is given in the presence of the patient; the hearing, to be sure, is held in private, and the place of the lay jury is taken by a lawyer and two psychiatrists. If the commission's finding is approved by the court (as it usually is), the patient is served with a document finding him of "unsound mind" and informing him that he suffers from a specified form of mental illness. Jury trial may be had upon demand. The results are hardly less traumatic than were the old mandatory jury trials which persisted until as recently as 1938.

There are two principal reasons why the legal authorities enter so actively into most of the commitments. One is that the public generally thinks of deprivation of liberty, regardless of place, as a function of the courts. Yet the public has no reluctance whatever about compelling the confinement of the tuberculous or of the person suffering from smallpox, plague, or leprosy. The courts, which recognize at once that they know nothing of such latter disorders, have no such hesitancy in passing on mental disorder. The other reason is the somewhat prevalent idea, fortunately being gradually dispelled, that many sane persons are improperly sent to mental hospitals and detained there—the so-called "railroading" myth. This belief was perhaps more widespread 80 years ago. Isaac Ray, in an article referred to earlier, blamed it largely on novels and periodicals. He said, "The castle and the convent and the poor debtors' prison as places for confining luckless heroes and heroines have given way to lunatic asylums. A story circumstantially and plausibly told is universally regarded as presumptively true, and if it is one of oppression and wrong, it enlists the deepest sympathies of the hearer." [56] He looked upon one of the prolific sources of this prevalent impression as the stories of the patients themselves. Somewhat philosophically, he added that legislation will not still all the public clamor; that, he said, will continue as long as the wrongful imprisonment of sane persons is capable of adding to the interest of a novel, or as long as the stories of the insane are received by credulous people as unqualified truths.

I have indicated earlier that there are persons, particularly in the early stages of mental disorder, who recognize full well that they are ill and who are ready to seek help, even to the extent of going to a hospital. Obviously, therefore, these patients should be given the privilege of entering voluntarily, and today in all but about five states a voluntary admission law is at least on the books. In some states the law is practically nugatory on account of the crowding of the hospitals. In some of the others, it is freely used—notably in Illinois, California, New Jersey, and Ohio. In each of those states, over 1,000 patients were admitted voluntarily in 1949, and in Illinois, over 3,700. It may be noted, in passing, that Massachusetts (1881) was the first state to provide for the voluntary admission of patients. Such a procedure is utilized to a very large extent in the English mental hospitals, and, indeed, in some of those institutions as many as 90 per cent of the patients are voluntary. The patient must, of course, be able to recognize that he needs care, must come in of his own free will, and is given an agreement to permit him to leave within a stated time (usually about three days) after he gives written notice. On very rare occasions it becomes necessary to detain such a person by legal means beyond that time if he is quite evidently a serious menace to himself or others, but the general policy is to try to meet the terms of the agreement. In an unpublished decision of a single justice of the Massachusetts Supreme Judicial Court, it was held 30 years ago that the proper practice is to obtain suitable legal authority by commitment proceedings in case a voluntary patient becomes so ill mentally as to cease to understand his voluntary status. This may be sound law, but it is somewhat dubious medical ethics.[57] The only published decision known to the author is a curious one from the New Mexico Supreme Court to the effect that the voluntary admission law of that state is violative of

due process and therefore unconstitutional, on the
ground that one cannot enforce a contract with a person whom he knows to be "so disordered in mind as
to require treatment in an institution for the treatment
of mental disease"! [58] Such a decision would seem to
be swimming against the medical tide.

Most of the admissions to private hospitals and the
veterans' hospitals are of a voluntary nature, and it is
likely that in the coming years this form of admission
will be more freely used than it has in the past. Certainly the time is approaching when there is a wider
recognition on the part of the medical profession and
of the general public that the mental patient is not on
so different a footing from the so-called nonmental
patient; in fact, it is an open question just where the
line comes, for certainly any patient who is physically
ill is hardly the same individual emotionally as when
he is feeling well, and many physical disorders have
marked mental concomitants, even to the extent of
psychosis!

With all the virtues of the voluntary admission law,
the fact remains that a great many patients are not
sufficiently aware of their need of mental hospital care
to enter voluntarily; therefore, some other way has to
be devised to procure for them that attention which
they should have. As a matter of the protection of the
public peace, there has long been a common-law right
to restrain an insane person against his will without
legal process whenever it is necessary to prevent damage
to person or property. In general, the right was only an
emergency one, however, and not only did the arresting

person act at his peril, but he was entitled to confine the allegedly ill person for only a reasonable time until proper proceedings could be held, legally authorizing his detention.[59] The element of dangerousness was paramount here, and, indeed, we still find this all too frequently in the statutes, tending, as Mr. Franklin N. Flaschner puts it in a very thoughtful article, to perpetuate the stigma of criminality attached to mental illness.[60] It is this attitude which accounts for the persistence of provisions for the "arrest" of mentally ill persons, their confinement in jail, and their being transported by the sheriff. An interesting anachronism is found expressed by the Alabama Supreme Court in these words: "The wise policy of the statute requiring that the sheriff take the person of the alleged lunatic into his custody is to bring the alleged lunatic notice by restraining him of his liberty, so that if he has any mind at all he will realize that he must defend in order to remove this restraint, and if not, persons interested in his freedom and property rights may come to his aid. Anything short of this cannot be approved as due process of law." [61] Such provisions do not belong in the law and should be promptly repealed wherever they may still exist. Massachusetts, incidentally, was one of the first states (in 1911) to forbid even temporary detention except in extreme emergency, in a lock-up, police station, or other place for the detention of criminals, placing the responsibility of such care upon the Board of Health.

The right of the state to protect the general welfare and the safety of the people is well recognized, being one of the powers which the states did not delegate to the federal government when the Constitution was adopted. As to the criteria for commitment, it would seem preferable to substitute for the concept of dangerousness to self or others the definition of a committable person offered by Judge Arthur E. Moore of Michigan: "A person who now is or with reasonable probability or certainty soon will become mentally ill to a degree which will so lessen the capacity of such a person to use his customary self-control, judgment and discretion in the conduct of his affairs and social relations as to make it advisable for him to be under medical and hospital treatment, care, supervision, or control, either for the protection of society or of the individual." [62] The Iowa Supreme Court well stated the purposes of commitment in these words: "The purpose of an inquisition of insanity is to aid and assist the individual, to provide means whereby the state may protect its unfortunate citizens, to furnish hospitalization so that the insane will have an opportunity to rehabilitate and readjust themselves into useful and happy citizens. It is not a criminal proceeding in any way. The restraint placed upon them is only until they have recovered so that they may again take their places in the communities from which they came. The confinement is not intended as punishment, but solely and only to provide the mentally sick with that environment which may possibly cure the disease and return them to society as useful citizens." [63]

In view of the fact that the courts are not in session daily, there should be some sort of emergency commitment procedure—some way whereby a patient in urgent need of hospital care and potentially dangerous may be sent to the hospital immediately. As a matter of fact, only about half of the states have what may be known as an emergency commitment: that is, compulsory confinement, usually for a stated, relatively brief, period, upon medical certification only, without the intervention of a court. At the end of this statutory period the patient either must be discharged or his status changed by voluntary admission or a formal commitment.

Other temporary provisions lacking the compulsory feature have demonstrated their usefulness. Massachusetts has perhaps the most informal arrangement of this sort, referred to as Temporary Care, which authorizes the admission to a mental hospital of a patient on the unsworn statement of a single physician or police officer or health officer.[64] This authorization is good for only 10 days, but it gives an opportunity for decision as to disposition and for formal commitment if that be necessary. It is worthy of note that nearly one-half of the patients admitted to the mental hospitals of Massachusetts enter on this certificate. From a long personal experience, I can vouch for the fact that I have never known, among the thousands of patients who have been admitted under this provision, of a single instance in which temporary observation was not reasonably indicated. I am convinced that "railroading" is one of the rarest of phenomena.

In some states, notably Maryland, the patient may be admitted on the certificate of two physicians and detained until he raises the question; that is, if he demands his release, steps may be taken for a formal court hearing.

All the states have a provision for a "regular" or formal commitment. There are numerous types, the most common one being a judicial hearing, with the judge making the final decision after an examination report by two physicians, these physicians meeting certain statutory requirements as to experience, residence, and disinterestedness. In some states there is an ad hoc, three-man commission, usually including a physician, and in some instances there is a standing commission, of which the judge or the clerk of court may be a member. In some states the matter is a court proceeding, whereas in others the docket is private and not an official court record. The latter method, which prevails in Massachusetts for example, is far kinder to the patient and to his family and tends to relieve much of the stigma which many families still feel.

The question of notice of the pending proceedings is one which has troubled psychiatrists and those interested in the welfare of the patient. Due process of law usually calls for some sort of notice and an opportunity to defend; yet it is a fact that, in some cases at least, the notice or the hearing would have extremely harmful effects upon the patient. They might precipitate flight, suicide, or exacerbation of the symptoms. In some states the judge is permitted to use his discretion on the matter of notice if in his opinion it would have a deleterious effect upon the patient to have notice served on him. In some instances the legal requirements are considered satisfied if some member of the family is given a notice and given an opportunity to appear at the hearing, but in about half of the states, presence at the hearing is required. To the patient this is often an extremely traumatic experience, especially that part which necessitates testimony in his presence by members of his family. Such testimony, given with the best of intentions, is not infrequently taken by the patient as being hostile.

It would seem that too many of the legal profession are inclined to equate commitment with criminal procedure and to lay undue stress upon the legal requirements, to the detriment of many patients. The *American Journal of Insanity* in 1868 pointed out that there should be "free and prompt access to mental hospitals and that we should not require 99 to be deprived because the hundredth may be surreptitiously deprived of his liberty." As Isaac Ray suggested, many men are arrested and yet found on trial to be innocent. Nevertheless, in such cases, he said, we are told very calmly that such wrongs are a part of the price we pay for public order and good government. In the same way, he indicated, we should run a few risks for the sake of protecting the overwhelming majority of the mentally ill.

It may be mentioned that complicated and legalistic provisions will not in and of themselves prevent improper commitments. Very few cases of this sort are reported in the decisions, but there are at least two on record which demonstrate that in this field too, people exist who will violate laws, regardless of how strict those laws may be. In a case heard by a federal court in Missouri, for instance, it was alleged that a dentist practicing in Kansas had been taken by his brother to Missouri, the brother then filing an "information" in the probate court, upon which the dentist was arrested, taken to jail, and then to the hospital, not being allowed to attend the hearing. The proceeding was wholly illegal; yet the fairly strict commitment laws of Missouri did not prevent it. In how many instances they have delayed the admission of patients in urgent need of hospital care one can only guess.[65]

One of the difficulties in commitment procedures is that in some jurisdictions commitment has become confounded and confused quite unnecessarily with the adjudication of incompetency. In the early days of the country, when the public "asylums" were only for the indigent, it was natural that some investigation of the financial status of the mental patient should be made in order that those legally responsible for him, if any, should arrange to pay for his care. This is not a proper function today, when the question of payment is quite secondary to eligibility for commitment. Today it is not generally agreed that the person must be indigent in order to be sent to a hospital. It is quite agreed, however, that if funds are available, the state should be reimbursed for the care of the patient to the extent of the equities of the situation.[66] The determination of the ability of responsible relatives to pay, however, is not a proper function of the court, but should be made by the supervisory body of the state *after* the patient has reached the hospital. The important thing is to procure care for the patient, regardless of his residence or ability to pay. Those matters may be settled at leisure after investigation, proper reimbursement arranged, and the nonresident returned to the state of his residence.

There is no reason in itself why a patient who has been committed to a mental hospital for care and treatment should be deprived of his civil rights any more than a patient who has been admitted voluntarily. It may be that the patient who is mentally ill and in need of hospital care has property, and that his illness may be such that he cannot adequately take care of it. It may be, indeed, that he cannot take care of his property even though he does not need to be in a mental hospital. The two situations, however, are not at all comparable and are not necessarily related. The order of commitment should, in the words of the Massachusetts Supreme Judicial Court many years ago, merely "afford justification for restraint." Indeed, that court has said that a man may be a proper subject for treatment and custody and yet have sufficient mental capacity to make a will, transact business, and be a witness.[67]

In those jurisdictions in which competency and commitment are dealt with in the one proceeding, many unnecessary complications are set up for the patient and his family, and serious hardship and expense may be caused—handicaps which may persist after release and interfere with the patient's rehabilitation. Most emphatically, commitment should not involve suspension of civil rights, and the statute should state clearly that the order of commitment has no effect upon guardianship proceedings. We may repeat that detention in jail should be prohibited and add that the patient, when ordered committed, should be taken to the hospital by someone other than a peace officer; in other words, every semblance of criminal procedure should be removed from the process of compulsory hospital care. Jury trial should be abolished, even as permissive, unless the constitution of the state involved demands it. Under the United States Constitution, there is no inherent right to a jury trial for commitment to a mental hospital.

Another corollary follows from what has been said about public suspicion of "railroading." This question comes up only, as a rule, in institutions which are operated for profit, rather than those which are operated by the state. It should not require much argument to demonstrate that in public institutions, of which the officials are officers of the state and in which, too, the overcrowding is, as a rule, so serious as to put pressure on them to discharge patients too early rather than to keep them too long, "railroading" is not very likely to occur; in other words, in the extremely remote event that a patient should be improperly sent to a mental hospital, he will not be detained longer than is necessary for the hospital to ascertain his true condition. This does not hold for private hospitals, particularly in those states where there is no central medical organization which has supervision over them. John Minson Galt of Williamsburg, one of the founders of the American Psychiatric Association, wrote as long ago as 1850, that "all asylums, public or private, should be placed under the immediate care of the Government" and that there should be a central authority—adding that there should, of course, be free entrance of visitors, both to public and private hospitals, and free communciation by the patient with his attorneys, with his relatives, and with his friends. Only if there is supervision by the state of private hospitals can those institutions be protected against the suspicion on the part of the public that they are, at times at least, maintaining patients there for the income which they receive, without regard to mental condition. Some private institutions are violently opposed to such supervision. It seems strange that they cannot recognize the fact that supervision of this sort would be their strongest protection. Such supervision presupposes a central supervisory body or commission under medical control, rather than a lay board. Such a body, too, should supervise and control the out-patient and other public psychiatric clinics; it should, in short, act as the "mental health authority." At present, it may be added, most states have a divided authority, one controlling and supervising the mental hospitals, the other (usually the public health department) operating the clinics provided by federal funds. Such a method has many disadvantages, and should not be continued. Many years ago it was suggested that it is wise for the left hand to know what the right hand is doing!

Various other types of persons suffer from mental derangement of one sort or another, for whom some special forms of compulsory detention in mental institutions are provided in the law. One might mention among these, for example, persons charged with crime and found unfit to plead, those who are acquitted of criminal charges by reason of insanity, or those who become mentally ill while serving sentence. In general, the states make special provisions for these groups, surrounding their release with certain precautions. Patients of this so-called "criminal insane" group are usually cared for in special wards or separate institutions. In the case of acquittal by reason of insanity, a provision similar to the English one for the indeterminate detention in a mental hospital of the defendant ("at Her Majesty's pleasure") would undoubtedly reduce considerably the criticism of acquittals of this sort. In homicide cases, Massachusetts has followed the example of England in requiring commitment to a state hospital "during his natural life" of any person acquitted by reason of insanity, release coming only as an act of grace from the Governor and Council upon recommendation of the Department of Mental Health.[68]

Details of the commitment of the mentally defective have not been discussed here, interesting though that subject is. Mental deficiency is a medical problem, although it has its educational aspects, and in most states the institutions for the mentally retarded are operated as psychiatric institutions, as they should be. The procedures for determining a condition of mental deficiency of sufficient grade to call for commitment to the care of the state are, in general, related in principle to the proceedings we have already discussed. A few states also have special provisions for the indeterminate segregation of offenders found to be mentally defective—so-called "defective delinquents." Such legislation was first enacted in Massachusetts in 1911.[69]

About 15 states now have provisions for another borderline group known as the "sexual psychopath"—a term which is open to considerable psychiatric criticism. There is a recognition that certain persistent sexual offenders are mental problems, and in the states having laws of this type, commitment for an indeterminate period is provided. In some instances, if treatment appears impractical, the patient may be returned to a correctional institution. I have discussed this type of legislation in an earlier chapter.

In a few states, provisions exist for the commitment of alcoholics and drug addicts as such. There is a growing interest in alcoholism, and it is being generally recognized as coming within the purview of psychiatry rather than as being amenable to the traditional "in and out" practice of imposing short and useless sentences to jail. Indeed, at present no less than 18 states are reported to have commissions either studying the problem of alcoholism or actually operating treatment programs for this group, usually of the out-patient variety rather than institutional. A few states, too, have special provision for the institutional care of epileptics, as distinguished from the general group of those suffering from mental illnesses.[70]

We have discussed at considerable length the principles which underlie the admissions to mental hospitals. What of release? We have seen that about three-fourths of the numbers admitted to mental hospitals in any given period are released within the same period.

In general the policy, except in the case of those who are considered recovered and discharged outright, is to release on a conditional basis, usually under social service supervision. This principle has been sustained by the courts.[71] It is highly desirable from the psychiatric point of view, as it gives the patient an opportunity to re-establish himself gradually in the community.

In 1885, the Commonwealth of Massachusetts, apparently inspired by the success of the practice which had been carried on for many years in Gheel, Belgium, adopted a plan for the boarding out of patients in families, or what is generally known as "family care." In fact, for many years Massachusetts was the only state to follow this practice. The patient was placed in a home under the supervision of the hospital, the caretaker was paid by the institution, and the patient was constructively considered to remain in the hospital.[72] It was not until 1933, spurred on by the depression, that other states adopted the example of Massachusetts; the practice is now fairly common.

As for return to the community, it seems logical that the hospital should be the organization to decide, except in the case of criminals; there, of course, the court should be consulted. Indeed, it is the general practice in criminal cases that, if charges are still pending, or if a portion of the sentence remains to be served, the prisoner, when pronounced recovered, shall be returned to the court or correctional institution, as the case may be. In the case of civil patients, however, it is the hospital physicians who are interested in restoring him to the community and who know best his condition.

Some patients, even after their admission to a hospital, fail to gain insight, and some become very insistent upon their release. They may, indeed, fancy that they are being held improperly and for ulterior motives by the hospital authorities. To them, as to all persons deprived of their liberty, wherever that may be, the writ of habeas corpus is available. The practices of the courts and, it may be added, of patients in mental hospitals, vary considerably from state to state. In Massachusetts for example, habeas corpus is initiated by a patient in a mental hospital with the utmost rarity, whereas in the District of Columbia several years ago, the Court of Appeals stated with accuracy that petitions for the writ are used not only as they should be, "to protect unfortunate persons against miscarriages of justice, but also as a device for harassing court, custodial, and enforcement officers with a multiplicity of repetitious, meritless requests for release." [73] In that decision, since overruled by the same court, it was held that the writ is available not for the purpose of determining a petitioner's mental condition, but instead is a method of initiating an appropriate procedure for that purpose.

The question may well be asked whether the judge, who sees the patient for a few moments in a courtroom, and on his best behavior at that, is in a better position to decide his fitness for release than is the hospital, the officials of which, like the judge, are servants of the public. About 25 years ago, the District of Columbia court released from Saint Elizabeths Hospital (over the objections of the hospital) a patient who within a

week of his release shot and killed the lawyer who had
represented him, and more recently a patient released
by court order committed suicide within a week. It
must be conceded, at least in the District of Columbia,
that discharges on habeas are rare; during the past year
for example, out of 58 different writs which were heard,
with, of course, numberless continuances and appear-
ances in court, the court released only three patients,
and as a matter of fact, one or two of those were on
the verge of being released by the hospital even before,
in their impatience, they filed the writ. I would not
be understood as advocating suspension or abolition of
the writ of habeas corpus; that would certainly not
be in the spirit of the United States Constitution. Nor
would I suggest that a patient might not sometimes
receive a certain amount of benefit by an opportunity
to "tell it to the judge." It seems reasonable, though,
that the court before ordering a patient discharged
should at least obtain psychiatric advice from an impartial source. In the District of Columbia, for example,
the court is at liberty to obtain a report from the Commission on Mental Health, a professional body which
is an arm of the court itself. Indeed, the Court of Appeals has stated, "It would be as unwise to discharge
such a person without a scientific determination as it
would be intolerable to compel the continued confinement of a person whose sanity has been restored." [74]
Indeed, it is likely that the assurance that the patient
may be heard on habeas corpus, at least once in a
while, is sufficient to meet the requirements of the
Constitution concerning due process of law. There are

some suggestions and some decisions, indeed, to the effect that the hearing need not necessarily be before the action is taken, so long as at some stage the patient has the right to be heard by the court.[75] A curious attempt to interpolate some source of authority between the state authority in charge of the mental hospitals and the courts was tried in Massachusetts in 1950, by establishing a board of appeal in the Department of Mental Health, no qualifications whatever being stated in the law as to the individuals on the board. According to newspaper accounts, the board was a fairly expensive investment on the part of the state, with very little return. In July of this year, the legislature refused to appropriate further funds for the board, so that it no longer exists. It should be pointed out that Massachusetts is one of the relatively few states which has a department of mental health, in charge of a commissioner of high professional qualifications, so the establishment of the board would have appeared to be a "work of supererogation."

Once the patient has been sent to the hospital, he is, of course, entitled to the best available care, and there is a responsibility on the part of the state to see to it that adequate facilities and adequate personnel are provided to give him the care which he needs. The records of some of the states have been quite unhappy in this regard, as we are all aware from the exposés and accounts which have appeared concerning the conditions in some of the public mental hospitals. The Governors' Conference of 1949 initiated a study of the status of the mental health programs of the states and made recommendations as to what further should be done. This was published in 1950, and provides a mass of material concerning the present status of the care given to patients in public mental hospitals.[76] The Council of State Governments is now conducting a further study of the training and research activities and possibilities of those hospitals. Certainly the patient should be protected from injury due to negligence; in short, the hospital should be held to the same standards of care and practice as general hospitals. As a matter of fact, courts have given several substantial judgments for injuries received by patients which were due to overcrowded or undermanned conditions in the hospital and for injuries caused by patients who had been negligently released.[77]

The public, too, is entitled to have some assurance that patients who are dangerous to the public are not permitted to leave the hospital, either with or without the permission of the institution, unless, of course, some court cares to release the patient on habeas corpus. One of the many prevalent popular delusions concerning mental patients is that no one really ever recovers, and that any patient who has been in a mental hospital should be looked upon forever after with suspicion. Such, of course, is far from being the case. In a study published in 1941, Dr. Horatio M. Pollock, statistician of the New York State Department of Mental Hygiene, discussed the question as to whether the paroled patient is a menace to the community. He came to the conclusion not only that the patient released from a mental hospital was a good risk from the point of view of criminal behavior, but that the rate of offenses among the general adult population was approximately 14 times as high as that among paroled patients! [78] A similar study in Connecticut,[79] involving 1,676 patients discharged over a four-year period, revealed that, although 233 of the patients had been known to the police before hospitalization, only 87 were so known after release, nearly all of them for such misdemeanors as drunkenness. The charge against the solitary patient accused of rape was, to say the least, of very dubious good faith. We may conclude, then, that the released patient is far from being a menace to peace and good order.

It is natural that now and then an offense, and sometimes a very lurid one, is committed by a person who has formerly been a patient in a mental hospital. Such a case arose in New York in July 1952, when a young veteran shot and killed an office worker at Columbia University. The young man, although he had been under psychiatric attention for several years, had never been a patient in a hospital since his discharge from military service. This offense led to a vitriolic outburst on the part of the judge before whom the defendant was arraigned. The rather startling statements, according to newspaper accounts, were made by the judge that "thousands of dangerous maniacs are released in utter disregard of the safety of the public," and that "it is better to confine a hundred potentially dangerous psychotics than to suffer the death of one innocent victim at the hands of a lunatic." He even went so far as to advocate prohibiting the discharge or parole of any "insane person" except upon application to a court, which court should have the inmate examined by impartial, qualified psychiatrists appointed by the court! [80] Quite aside from the lack of psychiatric knowledge of a good many judges, the question might be raised as to just where court psychiatrists would be found to examine all of the 184,000 patients who are discharged annually! The judge, of course, was wholly unfair to the physicians and the institutions, and quite unfamiliar with the fact that ex-patients of mental hospitals are, on the whole, considerably better conducted than the general run of the population. He made the common logical error of generalizing from a particular. The *Washington Post* (July 31, 1952), in commenting on this judicial outburst, said, "The crime committed by Peakes was a terrible tragedy, but the tragedy would be compounded if it were made the pretext for confining mentally ill persons indiscriminately or for supplanting psychiatry with demonology." No hospital, however careful, can guarantee the good behavior in perpetuum of any ex-patient; indeed, the good conduct of the so-called normal cannot be guaranteed! The hospital officials, who are best fitted to know the possibilities of the patient, take their social responsibilities seriously and do not release patients who are serious menaces. If all *possibly* troublesome patients were refused a trial in the community, however, the rate of overcrowding of our institutions would rise measurably. One proper function of a central medical supervisory body would be to supervise the release of unrecovered patients who are considered potentially dangerous; this is one of the many duties of the Massachusetts Department of Mental Health, for example.

The manner in which the newspapers can be counted upon to emphasize the link with a mental hospital may be indicated by the heading in a recent Washington paper, "Ex-Mental Patient Held in Knife Slaying of Baltimore Woman." Although the slaying occurred in September 1952, it turns out on close study of the "small print" in the news item that the person had been a patient in a state mental hospital in Maryland, but had been released in October 1949, nearly three years before the offense!

Mention has been made of the fact that the Federal Security Agency has recently prepared and distributed a Draft Act Governing the Hospitalization of the Mentally Ill. This act embodies most of the principles which have already been discussed and has received wide attention in the various states. One new feature of the act should be mentioned, namely, that having to do with what the act terms "involuntary hospitalization." The act provides for certification by two designated examiners that they have examined the individual and that they are of the opinion (1) that he is mentally ill, and (2) because of his illness is likely to injure himself or others if allowed to remain at liberty, or (3) is in need of care or treatment in a mental hospital and because of his illness lacks sufficient insight or capacity to make responsible application therefor. It will be noted that the old concept of dangerousness has been modified here. The proposal will probably receive the criticisms of the legal profession as going beyond the principle of *parens patriae* and the public health and the police powers of the state. It is, in all probability, safe to say that it is more in tune with the concepts of public welfare than the old idea of mere "dangerousness." The Draft Act is in line with modern standards of the care of the mentally ill, and is motivated primarily by the consideration of the welfare of the patient, while at the same time protecting him against improper confinement.[81]

In 1944, the American Bar Association appointed a Committee on the Rights of the Mentally Ill. A few reports were made, but for several years the committee has apparently been quiescent. In one of its last reports (1948), the committee stated that it found that "public dissatisfaction is grounded in administrative abuses and lack of proper financing rather than the inadequacy of legal procedures." It added that there was a "lot of room" for improvements, but that a uniform state law was not practical.[82]

With the growing public interest and understanding, we may expect that the states will expand and improve their institutional and clinic facilities for the treatment of the mentally ill, and that gradually the laws relating to this large group of men, women, and children will be brought more fully into line with the modern concept of regarding the mentally ill person as a patient, to be treated as are the other sick, not as a "dangerous" individual to be "committed" as a quasi-criminal.

IV

THE PSYCHIATRIST AS WITNESS

THERE ARE many types of legal action in which questions of motivation, mental fitness, or competency may arise. Thus it is not strange that in the field of psychiatry, as in the other branches of medicine, physicians are likely to have occasion to appear in court and to testify. Sometimes they testify as to facts within their knowledge concerning patients whom they have examined, but often, too, they will be asked to give their opinion, based upon those facts which have come to their attention. In other cases they may be asked to testify on the basis of facts which are presumed or hypothesized to be true, but about the truth or falsity of which they do not know from personal experience. In such cases they are allowed to testify on the ground that they have unusual knowledge, based on training and experience which is over and beyond that possessed by the ordinary man. Such witnesses are usually referred to as experts, and their type of evidence as opinion or expert evidence.

There is nothing new in the concept in the English law that there are facts which are unknown to the average man. As far back as the middle of the fourteenth century a case (of mayhem) is recorded, for example, in which a physician was called in to testify as to the nature of wounds, and in 1554, we find a court praising the practice of calling in experts to advise it. One of the early cases (1665) involved one of the most famous doctors of English history, Sir Thomas Browne, who testified that there were such things as witches.[83] In that case his evidence was an important and perhaps deciding factor in causing the jury to send to their deaths two poor old women who, it is recorded, "confessed nothing" before their execution! Sir Thomas, of course, was speaking of things of the existence of which he did not know from experience or observation, although in those days "everybody knew" there were witches—an excellent illustration of the fact that often those things which "everyone knows" are far from the truth, and of the further fact that experts *have* been known to testify on matters concerning which their knowledge was at least tenuous! As another example may be cited a case which shows how rapid are the strides we have made in our knowledge of contagious diseases. In 1884, in a suit for abatement of a nuisance (smallpox hospital), experts voiced violent disagreements as to the distance within which the "particles" from the patients could poison the air; one group testified to 2½ miles as the safe distance, while the other group thought 50 yards or less sufficient. They all admitted, however, that "science [had not] settled how the disease came to an end, or how the infection was transmitted"; the verdict was for the defendants.[84]

In the earlier days, the doctor or other expert was called in by the judge, who was then one of the finders of fact along with the jury, because he was trained and experienced in his field and because he could help the court and jury to interpret the facts of the particular case. It was to be presumed that, according to the standards of those times, he was a capable specialist in his field and furthermore, his status as being a court appointee and an adviser of the judge gave him a certain amount of authority. By the middle of the seventeenth century, however, an entirely different situation came about. The judge retired to some extent into the background, becoming a sort of referee, and the finding of the facts was left entirely to the jury, guided only by the judge's rulings on points of law, his charge on the law, and in England at least, on the facts as well. It was therefore natural that the judge should give up the practice of appointing technical advisers and leave the presentation of evidence to the two parties in the case. Thus the partisan method of presenting facts and opinions arose, a method which has done much to bring expert testimony of all sorts, and notably psychiatric expert testimony, into a considerable degree of disrepute.

It should be emphasized at this point once again that physicians are far from being the only experts who testify in the law courts, and that in some other fields of specialized testimony discrepancies of fact and opinion are wide and occasionally even startling. The experts in real estate value,[85] in handwriting, and even in ballistics do not always agree, and in questions involving surgery and general medicine medical testimony is not always unanimous, yet the public seems to light upon the luckless psychiatric expert as the prototype and the chief sinner. They hear the psychiatrist referred to as venal, incompetent, an obstructer of justice, or worse. It should not be forgotten that most of the cases in which the psychiatrist has occasion to testify are civil rather than criminal. The cases have to do, for example, with traumatic neuroses, with wills, with questions of competency, and with matters relating to the commitment of patients to mental hospitals. Now and then, however, psychiatrists testify in a criminal case. Immediately there is a hue and cry. Two such cases constitute a "trend"; three constitute a "wave," and one would almost believe from the journalistic comments that in practically every criminal case there is a conflict of psychiatric opinion!

There has not been very much change in practice in the past 200 years, so perhaps it is not strange that we hear criticisms from long ago just as we do today. A plea of insanity, for example, was fortified by psychiatric expert testimony in the case of Earl Ferrers in 1760, and a hypothetical question was used in Hadfield's case in 1800; nor did the criticism lag far behind. Over 100 years ago an English court stated, "Hardly any weight is to be given to the evidence of what are called scientific witnesses. They come with a bias on their minds to support the cause in which they are embarked." [86] Along the same line, an eminent professor of the Harvard Law School recently stated in an article that "the medical expert has become a stench in the nostrils of upright judges," adding, "Alienists are notoriously available for prosecution and defense in sensational criminal trials. In other fields the evil is just as virulent but not so noticeable because the opportunities for its exhibition are fewer." [87] Indeed, there have been those who doubted whether psychiatry was properly a field of medical testimony! For example, in 1862, the Lord Chancellor of England stated on the floor of the House of Lords that "the introduction of medical opinions and medical theories into this subject [the criminal law] has proceeded upon the vicious principle of considering insanity as a disease." It is of some interest to note that as late as 1924, the holder of that same august office seemed almost as dubious, stating that "psychology is a most dangerous science to apply to practical affairs."

The first difficulty, then, came about through the at least apparent partisanship of the expert. Since he was presented to support the contentions of one side or the other and since he was paid for his services, he was immediately placed under the handicap of appearing to be biased. It is a fact, of course, that it is proper on cross-examination to ask an expert how much he is being paid, as testing his partiality. It is not, however, true except in the very rarest instances that a professional man's opinion is for sale. As Ray well put it, "Because a man's opinions are worth money, it does not follow that they are corruptly bought." The implication of venality is an unwarranted slur on the members of an honorable profession.

Another practice developed as a corollary of the change in the production of expert testimony. This has to do with the qualifications of the so-called expert. When the judge was the one who sought advice for the court it was likely that he would turn to the most qualified persons he knew. When the parties had to

produce the opinion evidence it was far more likely
that they would attempt to secure an expert whose
views they were sure would favor their own side, regardless of the degree of his professional competence.
We are all aware of the fact that the more experienced
and conscientious physician will tend less to dogmatic
utterance than the ignorant, who tends to make up by
bombast for his lack of knowledge. Unfortunately, it
is the dogmatist who by his positiveness and assurance
sometimes makes the most convincing impression on the
jury. We shall speak later of the question of the qualifications of psychiatric experts. For the present, we may
say simply that, although courts have the right to insist
that the expert state his qualifications and to require
that those qualifications satisfy the court,[88] the tendency
has been to permit almost any person holding the
degree of doctor of medicine to testify on any specialty,
psychiatric or otherwise, in the field of medicine. For
example, a Kentucky court recently said, "Any doctor
of sufficient training and experience must be considered
to be an expert on matters affecting the disability of
human minds and bodies, although . . . the more experience one has had with a particular ailment under discussion the more valued his opinion will be." [89] In
that particular case, three psychiatrists testified to con-
cussion and hemorrhage of the brain, while three general practitioners testified that the plaintiff had not suffered these injuries and was only partially disabled. The
jury chose to believe the general practitioners, and the
verdict was affirmed on appeal.

Perhaps one reason for the failure of courts to exert

themselves more actively in insisting on qualifications of psychiatric experts is the very prevalent popular belief, reflected to a considerable extent in the law and especially in some more recent rulings of courts, that mental disorder and drunkenness are matters which are within the "common observation of men of ordinary education and experience" and that therefore a layman is competent to express an opinion, on the ground, as a court recently stated it, "that it is impossible to describe the actions or symptoms which constitute a basis for the opinion." [90] This negative attitude, which discards practically all of medical knowledge, has been criticized by an Illinois court recently, in admitting the evidence of "Drunk-o-meter" findings. The court said, "Medical science recognizes 60 pathological conditions which produce symptoms similar to those produced by alcohol, yet the law permits non-expert lay witnesses to testify on the theory that sobriety or intoxication are matters of common knowledge." [91] Curiously enough, the recent tendency, according to some legal writers,[92] appears to be toward the freer use of what is referred to as lay opinion evidence. In view of the many prevalent misconceptions among the laity as to the nature of mental illness and the behavior of the mentally ill, it seems likely that if a jury is to be confused by the evidence of experts it is almost sure to be completely misled by the evidence of nonmedical opinion witnesses! The illogical nature of the practice of admitting lay opinion evidence on mental conditions was tellingly criticized in an article by Reynolds in 1939. He points out that in criminal cases, where the life of the accused may be at stake, "Any man, with or without any special knowledge or skill, is still allowed to express an opinion on a highly specialized and scientific matter." [93] Compare this attitude with the readiness of courts to declare lay evidence regarding cancer or its cure as of "little, if any, weight." [94]

What may be termed the classical theory of the expert was well stated some years ago in an Ohio case and may be summarized as follows: First, the ordinary witness will testify to facts only which are within his knowledge. Some exceptions are necessary, however. Witnesses who are shown to be skilled, learned, or experienced in a particular art, science, trade or business may give their opinions on a given state of facts. Finally, on matters within common observation and experience, a witness may state his opinion but must state the primary facts on which he bases the opinion. [95]

It is this phrase, "the given state of facts," which has given rise to one of the most troublesome features of expert testimony, namely, the hypothetical question. The theory back of the hypothetical question is that only the jury is competent to pass upon the truth or falsity of statements made in the course of evidence, and that therefore the expert in giving his opinion on the basis of fact must only *assume* that those facts are true. He may, indeed, be asked to assume facts which are directly contrary to his opinion, and in any event the person described in the hypothetical question is a mere abstraction. Futhermore, the tendency is naturally to include only the supposed facts which are favorable to the side represented by the propounder. Courts are not in agreement as to the proper degree of completeness of the set of facts assumed, or the extent to which the judge should exert himself to make sure that a fair picture of the pertinent testimony is presented. Some of these hypothetical questions have constituted the *reductio ad absurdum*. In the recent trial of Alger Hiss in New York, for instance, the hypothetical question asked of one of the psychiatrists consumed, as we have noted earlier, 78 minutes in the reading. The record is said to have been set in a Massachusetts court in 1907 (in the famous Tuckerman will case), in which the hypothetical question consisted of 20,000 words and took several hours to read. (The answer—the ultimate in brevity—was, "I don't know"!)

A California court once described the picture presented by the hypothetical question as being "as false to the original as is a fantastic and distorted shadow cast by a flickering and uncertain light a false portrayal of the reflected object." [96] By means of the hypothetical question the expert may be put in a most unpleasant and unfair light. Furthermore, by being asked differing hypothetical questions by the two sides, he may in the eyes of a none-too-perceptive jury appear to be answering yes and no to the same question. In that case, of course, the jury is quite likely to throw out all of his evidence, substituting that somewhat dubious substitute for informed knowledge, "common sense." The use and abuse of the hypothetical question have received much attention from legal writers of late. We shall advert later to some of the possible remedies for this feature, which Judge Learned Hand once termed "the most

horrific and grotesque wen on the fair face of justice,"
and to which Dean Wigmore referred as "misused by
the clumsy and abused by the clever," and leading to
"intolerable obstruction of the truth."

Another objection on the part of the public is that
experts disagree, and that expert testimony may have
the effect of confusing and distracting the minds of the
jury at the very moment when they need to be self-
confident and sure. This is a strange objection indeed,
since in almost every case tried in the courts there is
a difference of ordinary or factual evidence, and in each
case the judge or jury must make up their minds as
to which set of witnesses comes the nearest to giving an
accurate statement of the truth. Witnesses, lay or expert,
are not the only persons who disagree. In every field
of activity there are differences of opinion: historians
and critics, for example, not to mention of course lawyers and judges. Indeed, when it comes to expert testimony, the lawyers may be depended upon to develop
any differences of opinion and to make them appear as
great as possible!

We have mentioned some of the objections to expert
testimony, particularly of the psychiatric variety, on
the part of judges, lawyers, and the public. What of
the physician? What are his views? Why is it that he
often hesitates to enter the arena of the courtroom?
One reason, which may seem trivial but which to a
busy man is not, is the amount of time involved in
the actual court proceedings. To be sure, lawyers as
a rule attempt to save the physician as much time as
possible, but there are inevitable delays in court pro-

ceedings which the lawyer cannot always foresee and which may result in losing several days, rather than an hour or two, from a busy practice.

More important than this, perhaps, is the adversary atmosphere of the whole proceeding. The physician is accustomed to having the patient come to him in his office, seeking help, and to take the necessary time to make the examinations, obtain the history, arrive at a diagnosis, and outline a course of treatment. If the patient has been examined by other persons, the physician will obtain the reports of the radiologist or pathologist and may consult with the other physicians. In a court proceeding all this is changed. In most jurisdictions he will not be permitted to express an opinion which is based in whole or in part upon statements which have been related to him by other persons than the defendant, unless those statements are introduced in evidence and "hypothesized" to him in the form of a question. For example, in a murder case in North Carolina not long since, a new trial was ordered because the pathologist had based his diagnosis of carbon monoxide poisoning, in part at least, on a chemist's report— that report being "hearsay" and therefore objectionable.[97] This all seems very strange to the physician, and quite unpleasant. Again, he may be given inadequate time to make the necessary examinations of the person concerning whom he is to testify. What is worse, in some instances, the attorney will object to his consulting with the physicians who have been retained by the opposing counsel.

When he mounts the stand, he is asked questions in

terms of legal concepts. This is, of course, necessary, since after all, it is a court of law in which he is testifying. The language, nevertheless, is alien to him. He does not think in terms of right and wrong, for example, or of the effect of a particular delusion upon a particular action. He is likely to be asked to give yes or no answers, although he knows full well that he cannot in most cases be dogmatic, and that in fairness to himself and the court he should explain the significance of his replies to the case at issue. Underlying the questions is the assumption that there is a direct causal chain and a unitary cause of any particular symptom—again an assumption which is often contrary to fact. In the case of demands for dogmatic answers, or in the case of unfair methods of cross-examination, the physician is always at liberty to appeal to the judge, and as a rule the judge will keep the counsel within bounds and permit the witness to explain his views and the reasons for them.

The physician may find that he is badgered with opinions of laymen concerning the sanity of the person concerning whom the litigation is going on—opinions which, although they may be meaningful to the jury are likely to be unsound medically. He is likely to have a hypothetical question posed to him and to be asked to assume facts which may be entirely irrelevant or even contradictory and to which he cannot give an opinion which he considers professionally sound. Much again depends on the attitude of the judge, some being very strict in the hypothetical questions which they allow and others singularly lax. If he should be unfortunate enough to be testifying before a judge who has an attitude reflected in the New York dictum of many years ago, that it "is generally safer to take the judgments of unskilled jurors than the opinions of hired and generally biased experts," [98] he is likely to be embarrassed on more than one occasion during the course of his testimony. Finally, he may even find himself compared by the jury with some of his colleagues whom he knows not to be well equipped in the specialty in which they are testifying but whose testimony has been admitted by a judge who is not inclined to draw very strictly the lines of qualifications.

Such are some of the reasons why we find physicians who hesitate to enter the courtroom. There are reasons for many of the situations to which they object, and some of them have existed for a long time. That does not necessarily mean that they are incapable of any sort of amelioration or cure, nor should it be thought that those interested in the problem have been idle or negligent. Judges, lawyers, professors of law, and physicians have worked long and diligently in attempting to devise methods of improving the status of expert testimony and its use. In 1883, for example, Sir James Fitzjames Stephen, an eminent judge and writer on legal affairs, emphasized the importance of fairness and competence, and advocated especially joint examination by the experts who had been selected by both parties— a proposal which we find much later, for example, in the Federal Rules of Criminal Procedure.

We have spoken so far almost exclusively of civil actions and deliberately omitted discussion of criminal proceedings, partly because of their negligible number in spite of their notoriety, and partly because they have been fully treated by many other writers, notably by Professors Sheldon Glueck and Henry Weihofen. It should be pointed out, however, that if any correction is possible, it should be easier to bring it about on the criminal than on the civil side of the court. In civil cases, the state acts largely as an arbiter, so that it is difficult to control the temptations which are caused by the personal and pecuniary interests of the parties. On the criminal side, however, the state has a dual interest because it is at once the prosecutor and the protector of the rights of the accused, the *parens patriae;* there are, theoretically at least, no conflicting personal or pecuniary interests. It is largely for this reason, then, that the attempts at legislative reform have been aimed especially at criminal prosecutions, with only a minor interest in civil cases.[99] One of the early proposals (1897) was offered by the Massachusetts Medicolegal Society and the Massachusetts Medical Society, namely that a panel of experts be set up from which the court might appoint. Unfortunately, however, this bill was never enacted. As early as 1905, too, Michigan passed a law limiting the numbers and the fees of expert witnesses; probably the limitation of the number of such witnesses was already an inherent right of the courts.[100] One of the very significant early attempts was made in 1909, in the state of Washington, providing that insanity should be no defense to a charge of crime, and that if the defendant were found to be mentally ill the court should order him committed to a state hospital until recovered. Unfortunately, this law was held unconstitutional in the Strasburg case.[101]

Beginning about 1915, the Institute of Criminal Law and Criminology set up a distinguished committee, the chairman of which, Professor Edwin R. Keedy, of the University of Pennsylvania, is still an active worker and writer in the field of law. Professor Keedy and his legal associates were supported by three eminent psychiatrists: Dr. Morton Prince, of Boston, Dr. Adolf Meyer, of Johns Hopkins, and Dr. William A. White, then Superintendent of Saint Elizabeths Hospital, of Washington, D.C. That committee, known as Committee B, proposed that the court be given the specific right to summon witnesses, not, of course, precluding either party from using other experts; that no testimony concerning the mental condition of the accused should be received from his witnesses until the witnesses summoned by the prosecution had been given an opportunity to examine the accused; that commitment to a mental hospital for observation be permitted; that written reports from the witnesses be permitted, subject to cross-examination; and that consultation of witnesses be encouraged.[102] In 1921, Wisconsin passed a statute providing for the appointment of experts by the court—an act which was subsequently declared constitutional.[103]

Indeed, it is quite likely that this law was supererogatory; at least it is probable that courts have the inherent right to summon experts, except in the states of Illinois and Michigan, in which the courts have made some curious decisions forbidding the practice. At least 20 states have statutes which expressly authorize the courts to appoint experts and report, and the same provision is found in the Federal Rules of Criminal Procedure. There have been other legislative attempts, but we need not discuss them at length here.

There is one piece of legislation which is of particular interest to a Massachusetts audience and which has pointed the way to a new approach in the matter of the mental state of persons accused of crime. I refer to the Briggs Law of Massachusetts, originally enacted in 1921, through the activity of Dr. L. Vernon Briggs, a prominent Boston psychiatrist.[104] Briefly the law provides that when a person is indicted for a capital offense, or whenever a person who is known to have been indicted for any other offense more than once or to have been previously convicted of a felony is indicted or bound over for trial, the clerk shall notify the Department of Mental Health, whereupon the Department shall cause such person to be examined with a view to determining his mental condition and the existence of any mental disease or defect which would affect his criminal responsibility. A small fee is allowed the examining physician. The report itself is not admissible, but the physicians who have made the examination may be called to testify by either party. First, the examination is conducted by neutral, impartial experts. Second, these experts are selected by a professional department of the administrative branch of the government, namely, the Department of Mental Health. Third, the examination is applicable to all defendants who fall within certain clearly defined legal categories, and is not dependent upon the supposed recognition of mental disease by the judge, defense attorney, or jail attendant.

Ideally, perhaps, all offenders should be examined before trial, but as this is not feasible, a selection is made by applying the law to presumably the more serious category of offenders. On the various occasions when the law has been attacked, it has been upheld, and the Supreme Judicial Court of the Commonwealth in an early case pointed out, "The examination may fairly be assumed to have been made by competent persons, free from any disposition or bias, and under every inducement to be impartial and to seek and ascertain the truth." [105] A considerable literature has developed on the *modus operandi* of the Briggs Law. Since it applies essentially to criminal cases, those interested are referred to the articles which have appeared in the literature. Briefly, the recent study by Dr. P. B. Hagopian,[106] the Assistant Commissioner of the Department of Mental Health, covering a total of approximately 6,600 cases, showed that of this number approximately 19 per cent were found to be in some way suggestively or definitely abnormal mentally: 1.2 per cent psychotic, 6.1 per cent recommended for observation in a mental hospital, 5.5 per cent feeble-minded, 5.4 per cent of borderline intelligence, and other conditions .8 per cent. The significant thing about the Briggs Law is that it has obviated the battle of the experts in criminal cases in Massachusetts, that it has provided for the prompt recognition of defendants who should be in hospitals, thus preventing trial of mentally ill persons, and that competent, unbiased examinations have been given to all persons who fell within the legal range of the law. So far, the law has been emulated only in Michigan and in Kentucky.

An example of the sort of situation which can be avoided by an automatic reference such as is provided by the Briggs Law may be summarized briefly.[107] In December 1943, one Louis Wolfe killed his wife. The trial, in October 1944, resulted in a conviction of murder in the first degree, and at the close of the trial, the prisoner harangued the court in such a way that grave doubt was set up concerning his mental state. He was accordingly committed to Bellevue Hospital for observation and shortly thereafter was committed to Matteawan State Hospital. In February 1950 (over five years from the time he was received), Matteawan reported that he was no longer insane and returned him to court, but at the hearing on their report, the doctors from Matteawan reversed their opinion. Other doctors were assigned by the court, who reported that the defendant was capable of defending himself, although the evidence seems to indicate that their examinations were, to say the least, sketchy. The court confirmed the original report of Matteawan, to the effect that the prisoner was sane, and imposed sentence. Later a motion for a new trial was offered on the ground that the defendant had been insane when he was tried in 1944, and was granted. On an appeal by the District Attorney, however, the order for a new trial was overruled by the Appellate Division of the Supreme Court, which reinstated the death sentence. The entire proceedings were reviewed by the Court of Appeal, and the sentence was affirmed.

In June 1952, the sentence was commuted by Governor Dewey to life imprisonment. If it were not for the fact that a man's life had been at stake in these proceedings, this case might be almost referred to as a comedy of errors. Certainly it resulted in a vast waste of time and subjected a mentally ill patient to some stresses which the law never intended should be imposed on any defendant suffering from mental disorder. Had the Briggs Law or a similar automatic reference been in force in New York at the time, his mental condition would have been reported to the court before the trial began, and Wolfe would have been sent promptly to a mental hospital without any trial on the charges.

As another instance, one may mention a recent Illinois case.[108] The defendant, sentenced for robbery in November 1931, had been adjudged incompetent and insane in Los Angeles the preceding January—a fact not known to the Illinois court at the time of sentence. In January 1949, the convict filed a writ of error alleging insanity at the time of trial, and a new trial was ordered on the ground that a judicial determination of incompetency continues in force until superseded by a later determination of competency!

We have spoken earlier of the fact that originally the courts appointed expert advisers, and that this practice had lapsed into disuse; further, that the courts in most states probably still have the right to make such appointments. Indeed, in some states it has been specifically held that the court may charge the jury on the fact that the expert has been appointed by the court—in other words, that his status, which presumably means that he is free of bias, may be called to the attention of the jury as affecting his credibility. This attitude is not unanimous. In the state of Delaware, for example, where a statute permits the court to appoint experts in physical injury cases, it has been held that once the expert is called, even though he has been appointed by the court, he becomes the witness of the party calling him, thus losing any status he had earlier as a neutral.[109]

In Massachusetts, the law goes even farther. There it is provided that any court of the Commonwealth may, in any case coming before it, ask the Department of Mental Health to assign a physician to make a mental examination of "any person coming before the court," a service which is rendered gratis. In the only case which has been decided by the Supreme Judicial Court of the Commonwealth,[110] it was held that this applied to civil as well as criminal cases, and to plaintiffs as well as to defendants. It was not decided that the court could go so far as to order the mental examination of a witness; hopefully that decision will be made at some time in the future, as there certainly are cases where it would be highly desirable. Here is a very wide statute, which provides free and expert and unbiased advice to the court, but which is utilized almost not at all, in spite of the vast number of personal injury and other civil damage cases as well as criminal cases which come before the various courts. In 1934, for example, 37 requests were made, 34 of them in criminal cases, while during the same period, in all the courts of the Commonwealth, nearly a quarter-million cases of one sort or another were heard or entered! Although the courts may order defendants in criminal cases committed to mental hospitals for observation, it is questionable whether they would have such a right in civil cases unless a party to the case became so acutely mentally ill in court as to cause a disturbance.

As far as civil cases are concerned, the most important contribution has been the Uniform Expert Testimony Act, since incorporated almost completely in the Model Code of Evidence proposed by the American Law Institute. The astonishing thing about this proposal, which was devised by a committee of distinguished attorneys under the chairmanship of Dean Albert J. Harno, of the University of Illinois Law School, is that it has been adopted, aside from the Federal Rules of Criminal Procedure, only (in part) by the state of Vermont,[111] and in the Rules of the Supreme Court of South Dakota. The fact that after the lapse of 15 years this proposal is in force in only two states and in the federal courts reminds one of a remark made many years ago by Dr. Henry Maudsley, the distinguished English psychiatrist, in discussing the question of expert testimony, to the effect that "our legal dignitaries have not the least desire to be helped out of their dilemma"! The fundamental principles of the Uniform Expert Testimony Act are, in brief: The court is given the authority to appoint expert witnesses, either on its own motion or on the request of either the state or defendant in a criminal proceeding, or of either party in any civil proceeding, this number being limited to three on each issue. The court gives notice to the parties when it appoints witnesses, and the parties are required to notify the court when they call expert witnesses of their own. The court is encouraged to bring the parties to an agreement as to the experts desired, and if the parties agree, the court appoints the experts upon whom there is agreement. The witnesses appointed by the court are to make such examination and inspection of the person or subject matter as they deem necessary for a full understanding and are to be permitted access to the persons, things, or places under investigation, for the purpose of inspection and examination. The experts are to file written reports under oath. This report may be read, subject to objections as to the admissibility of any part thereof. The court, too, may permit or even require a conference before the trial on the part of some or all of the expert witnesses, and two or more of them may unite in a report which may be introduced. Any of these witnesses may be called to testify in court, subject to cross-examination, with reasonable limitations upon the number so called. In the case of the court-appointed experts, the fact that the expert has been appointed by the court is to be made known to the jury. The witness may be asked to state his inferences, whether they are based upon his personal observation, evidence introduced at the trial, or on his technical knowledge of the subject, without first specifying hypothetically in the question the data on which these inferences are based. He may, too, be required to specify the data on which his inferences are based. Finally, his compensation is fixed by the court and taxed as costs of the case.

It will thus be seen that nearly all of the objections which we have mentioned above, with the one exception of lay opinion evidence, are covered by this model act, and it is certainly to be hoped that it will be incorporated in the rules of procedure or the laws of all of the states in the very near future. Its adoption would go far toward curing the grounds of criticism of expert testimony in all fields.

Of course, we must admit that the court appointment of experts does not necessarily mean that they are unimpeachable. Some courts seem to have strange ideas about the qualifications of experts. Recently, for example, the Illinois Supreme Court said, "While physicians are better qualified to testify to a diseased condition than a layman, their testimony upon the subject of the mental capacity of an individual whom they have been privileged to observe is not entitled to any greater weight than that of laymen." [112] Again, a Texas court,[113] which had not seen the witness or talked with him, ruled that the lower court had made an error in excluding as an expert a general practitioner who said that, although he had read casually on psychiatry, he did not hold himself out as an expert, thus setting itself up as a better judge of qualifications than the doctor himself! The scandals which led to the passing of the Desmond Act in New York in 1939 are well remembered. Before that time the courts of New York City were authorized to appoint "lunacy commissions" of not more than three "disinterested persons"; many of these commissions were made up of nonmedical persons or general practitioners whose chief qualification seemed to be that they were related, or otherwise close, to the judge! On the other hand, some judges have hesitated to appoint experts on the ground that they were not judges of expertness in fields other than the law, or that they found it difficult to find experts who had no previous commitments or biases.[114]

If we review the historical evolution of expert testimony, it seems elementary to say that the courts should insist on qualifications. In general, they assume that any physician may testify on any topic in the field of medicine. In the field of psychiatry this is certainly unrealistic, in view of the wholly inadequate training in psychiatry which medical students, until very recently at least, have received, and the all-too-general lack of interest of the medical profession which still prevails in the matter of mental disorder. It was the persistent appearance in court of unqualified so-called "experts" in psychiatry that led the American Psychiatric Association to establish in 1934, in conjunction with the American Medical Association and the American Neurological Association, the American Board of Psychiatry and Neurology. Requirements for certification by this board are high, and although a certificate from the board does not prove that a psychiatrist is an experienced witness, it may be looked upon as certifying to his professional competence in the field of psychiatry. It is my earnest hope that eventually courts, wherever diplomates in psychiatry are available, may come to look upon certification by the board as a prerequisite to the giving of expert testimony in the field of psychiatry, or at least that the court will question closely the qualifications of any nondiplomate who is presented as an expert.

There are other possibilities, some of which are in practical operation. For example, in the District of Columbia, the District Court has a Commission on Mental Health, which is its official professional medical adviser in matters of the commitment of mentally ill persons to institutions. A number of courts, particularly on the criminal side, have clinics operated by the court to advise, especially in the disposition of persons who have been found guilty. The function of such clinics could well be widened, and their number increased, with profit to the courts. The earliest one of these was set up in the Boston Municipal Court by Dr. V. V. Anderson, as far back as 1913, and there are excellent ones, for example, in the Court of General Sessions of New York City, the Supreme Bench of Baltimore, and the Recorder's Court of Detroit. The number of these, however, is small, perhaps not exceeding 10. In civil cases it might well be that administrative tribunals or groups of expert investigators might act similarly to the method by which courts appoint masters or auditors in certain types of litigation now, or perhaps to the English method of having boards of assessors sit with the court. Chief Judge Stephens of the Circuit Court of Appeals for the District of Columbia summarized the advantages some years ago as enlarging judicial discretion, simplifying pleadings, and raising the level of dignity of the trial to a serious search for justice in the public interest, not a mere victory for a party.[115]

An improvement in the utilization of psychiatry in the administration of the law is not, however, wholly a question of laws or of administrative machinery. If judges, by their carelessness about the qualifications of witnesses and about the type of hypothetical questions they permit, are partly to blame, we cannot entirely exculpate the lawyers. To be sure, the lawyer has as his job the winning of the case for his client; but there are rules of procedure and certain generally accepted canons of proper conduct. Most lawyers are above reproach, but there are a few who forget that when the expert is on the stand they are dealing with another professional man, and their attitude sometimes is hardly so courteous as should be expected. There are times, too, when unfair advantages are taken in the line of badgering and attempting to confuse.

Nor is the physician himself blameless. There are certain general rules at least which he should follow in an attempt to maintain decent standards of professional conduct and attitude. He should, of course, be sure that he has a reasonable grasp of the problem about which he purports to speak as an expert, not only in general but as to the particular case; that is, he should satisfy himself that he has made an adequate examination and that he has before him the same sort of information as he would wish in making a diagnosis in his office. He should insist, too, on making a joint examination with the experts retained by the other side. This is sometimes objected to by the attorneys. In that case, the expert may properly remember that he is acting voluntarily and that he is not compelled to accept the invitation to appear. By having a joint examination, as is suggested in the Uniform Expert Testimony Act, the likelihood of disagreement is far less. He should by all means insist that whatever fee he may charge be paid, regardless of what his testimony may be. Contingent fees should be entirely taboo—that is, fees the payment of which is dependent upon the outcome of the case. The expert, too, should bear in mind that he may properly be asked on the stand what fee he is charging and under what circumstances it is to be paid. He should not act in court as an "assistant counsel"; he should avoid sitting at the desk with the attorney, for example, or prompting the attorney on questions to be asked of the experts on the opposing side. If a physician does this, he should certainly refuse to appear as witness also. He will do well if he leaves the courtroom when his testimony is completed, rather than appearing to show too much curiosity about the outcome of the case and the effect of his evidence. He should bear in mind always that he is in the courtroom as an adviser to the court, not as an advocate for a party, and that it is his duty to answer questions fairly and honestly within the scope of his ability. If he does not know the answer to a question, he should say so. He should, in the words of an English physician in a recent article, "satisfy his conscience upon oath to tell the truth, as far as he saw it, the whole truth, as far as it is known, and nothing but the truth, so as to avoid perjury. No one, certainly, can do more." [116] Finally, when it comes to making his decision as to appearing, he should bear in mind that as a member of the community and a member of a class which has certain privileges and prerogatives, he should, if he can do so conscientiously, be willing to aid the administration of justice and make his knowledge available to the court. "Doctors," said Isaac Ray, referring to testimony in court, "are bound by more than the Hippocratic oath, to serve as faithful ministers of science, casting aside every ignoble prepossession born of the time and place." [117]

Morals and ethics cannot very well be legislated, no matter what legal provisions may be set up, and there is always a possibility that lawyers will be tempted to utilize persons who have inadequate qualifications or who may be on the verge of charlatanism and venality. In 1940, the Minnesota State Medical Association and state Bar Association established what has come to be known as the Minnesota Plan. A committee on expert testimony has been appointed, and any judge, attorney, or physician may make complaint in writing to the committee if in his opinion any medical expert has knowingly and willfully testified improperly. The entire transcript of the evidence is then studied, information is obtained from specialists in the field involved, and the committee then takes whatever steps appear to be indicated. The Plan has worked well, and its very existence has operated to discourage improper conduct.[118] In the last analysis, a profession like the law or medicine must police itself if it is to maintain the respect of the community.

In *Collier's Weekly* for May 12, 1951, Mr. Albert Q. Maisel reported the results of an opinion poll which had been taken under the direction of Elmo Roper in Louisville, Kentucky, relative to the attitudes concerning psychiatry. The answers to certain questions were obtained from about 4,000 persons, representing old and young, lawyers, physicians, businessmen, housewives, and so on. It was found that throughout the survey, physicians, clergymen, and teachers showed themselves to be in far closer accord with modern psychiatric methods than did the lawyers. Only in the legal profession was there found to be a relatively large measure of distrust of psychiatry. Nearly 25 per cent of the lawyers, for example, favored punitive treatment for the juvenile delinquent; more than 40 per cent voted against the proposition that it is worth while to obtain a psychiatrist's help when someone begins to act strangely; and more than two-thirds of them endorsed secrecy about family mental illness. They departed from the general pattern, says Maisel, on such other points as the charge that mental patients are maltreated in hospitals and on the question about the experts' ability to agree on a psychiatric diagnosis. These findings are mentioned because they emphasize the need of desensitization not only of lawyers but of doctors regarding each other and their common aims. In a number of universities (Tulane, Illinois, George Washington, Texas, and Yale, for example), joint seminars are held between law and medical students. The seminar on medicolegal problems which has been announced for the Harvard Law School during the coming year is particularly welcome; it is to be conducted under the auspices of both the law and medical schools, with discussions of various medicolegal problems by lawyers and physicians. Isaac Ray said a hundred years ago that what is needed is "a higher sense of professional honor among lawyers and doctors and a healthier public sentiment. To the development of those, mutual understanding will contribute much."

The doctors and the lawyers of the future will understand each other better than is now the case.

A thought which is possibly somewhat irrelevant is this: We have seen that the greatest criticism of psychiatric expert testimony is voiced by the public in connection with criminal cases, and almost always in connection with criminal cases in which the death penalty may be invoked. It may be that on some future occasion there will be opportunity to discuss some of the aspects of the criminal law, particularly the disposition of offenders. For now, however, simply for what it may be worth, it is my considered opinion that capital punishment has no place in the modern scheme of penal treatment and that if capital punishment were abolished nearly all of the public furor against psychiatric expert testimony would disappear. This statement, however, may be considered, in the language of the judges, as an *obiter dictum*.

There is much room for improvement in the use of psychiatric expert testimony. Some of the improvement may be brought about without change in the existing law; in other instances legislation would be desirable. In the words of John Stuart Mill, "Improvement consists of bringing our opinions into clearer agreement with facts; we shall not be likely to do this while we look at facts only through glasses colored by those very opinions." We may safely expect that with the development of mutual understanding between the representatives of law and psychiatry the adoption of the needed improvements which we have discussed may be accelerated.

REFERENCES

1. Barry v. Chaplin, 74 Cal. App. 652, 169 Pac. (2nd) 442 (1946). Held that such tests are not conclusive because not so declared by Code! McComb, J., in special opinion, reluctantly concurring, stated very aptly "To reject the new and certain for the old and uncertain does not tend to promote improvement in the administration of justice" (at 453).

2. Jordan v. Mace, 144 Me. 351, 69 A 2nd 670 (1949). "If the jury may disregard the fact of non-paternity, clearly demonstrated, . . . the purpose and intent of the legislature, that the light of science be brought to bear on a case such as this, are given no practical effect."

    See also S. B. Schatkin. "Paternity Proceedings—A Changing Concept." 42 J. Crim. Law 821 (1952).

3. For further details the reader is referred to K. A. Menninger's *The Human Mind* (3rd ed. 1945), Leon J. Saul's *The Bases of Human Behavior* (Lippincott, 1951), or any standard textbook of psychiatry (Noyes, Henderson & Gillespie, or Strecker, Ebaugh & Ewalt, for example).

4. See Everson, G. "The Human Element in Justice." 10 J. Crim. Law 90 (1919) and Branham and Kutash's *Encyclopedia of Criminology* (1949), article on "Sentencing Behavior of Judge," pp. 449-461.

5. Lancet, vol. 1 of 1939, no. 25, p. 1419 (June 24, 1939).

6. 21 Am. Bar Assoc. J. 271 (1935).

7. R. v. Duncan and others 2 (1944) All E R 220.

8. Comm. v. Taylor, 16 Phila. 439 (1884).

9. St. v. Noel, *102 N.J.L.* 659, 133 Atl. 274 (1926). Comment in 32 Iowa L. R. 714 (1947).

10. *A General View of the Criminal Law of England* (1863), p. 90.

11. Lilly v. Comm. of Int. Rev. 343 U.S. 90 (1952).

12. St. v. Jones, 50 N.H. 369 (1871).

13. U.S. ex rel. Smith v. Baldi, 192 Fed. 2nd 540 (1951).

14. *Law and Literature* (1931), p. 100.

15. 99 U. of Pa. L. R. 267 (1950); see also Weihofen and Overholser, 56 Yale L. J. 959 (1947).

16. In re Moulton, 96 N.H. 370 77 Atl. 2nd 26 (1950).

17. G. L., ter. ed., c. 272 Sec. 34.

18. Cf. article by B. Karpman, 43 J. Crim. Law 13 (1952).

19. See B. M. Beck, *Five States,* published by Am. Law Institute, 1951.

20. See Manfred S. Guttmacher's excellent volume, *Sex Offenses* (1951), Paul Tappan's article on "Sentences for Sex Crimes," 42 J. Crim. Law 332 (1951), and the report of the Joint Comm. of the Brit. Med. Assn. and the Magistrates Assn., published by the Brit. Med. Assn. in 1949.

21. *Pleas of the Crown,* 635.

22. Roberts v. St., 106 Nebr. 362, 183 N.W. 557 (1921).

23. Yessen v. St., 228 Md. 316, 92 N.E. 2nd 621 (1950). See comment, 26 Ind. L. J. 98 (1950).

24. Am. J. Psychiat. 107:684 (1951).

25. See Wigmore on Evidence (3rd ed.) § 924 and note, 59 Yale L. J. 1324 (1950).

26. 22 Pa. Bar Assn. Quart. 140 (1951).

27. Coffin v. Reichard, 148 F 2nd 278 (1945).

28. Peo. v. Samuran, 408 Ill. 549, 97 N.E. 2nd 778 (1951).

29. Bouldin v. St., 87 Tex. Cr. App. Rep. 419, 222 S.W. 555.

30. 25 Cornell L. Q. 556 (1940).

31. Van Gundy v. Wilson, 84 Ga. App. 429, 66 S.E. 2nd 93 (1951).

32. Hoffer v Burd, —— N D ——, 49 N.W. 2nd 282 (1951). See also Wigmore on Evidence (3rd ed.) § 1919.

33. Arridy v. Peo., 103 Colo. 29, 82 P 2nd 757.

34. Graham v. Peo., 95 Colo. 544, 38 P 2nd 87 (1934).

35. Comm. v. Cox, 1951. Mass. Adv. Sh. 857, 100 N.E. 2nd 14 (1951).
36. Tuggle v. St., 73 Okla. Cr. Rep. 208, 119 Pac. 2nd 857 (1941).
37. Quercia v. U.S., 289 U.S. 466 (1933).
38. Cole v. St., 170 Miss. 800, 150 So. 757 (1933).
39. Ex parte Zanetti, 34 Cal. 2nd 136, 208 P 2nd 657 (1949).
40. Fulton v. Freeland, 219 Mo. 494, 118 S.W. 12 (1909).
41. In re Hart's Estate, 107 Cal. App. 2nd 60, 236 P 2nd 884 (1951).
42. In re Bickner's Estate, 259 Wis. 425, 49 N.W. 2nd 404 (1951).
43. Met. Life Ins. Co. v. Davis, 295 Ill. App. 382, 15 N.E. 2nd 874 (1938).
44. Note by Lubersky, W., vol. 18, p. 45 (1938).
45. 6 Moore, P. C. 341, 12 Jur. 949.
46. L. R. 5 Q. B. 549.
47. In re Gottsman, (N.J. Chancery), 48 A 2nd 800 (1946).
48. In re Higbee's Estate, 365 Pa. 381, 75 A 2nd 599 (1950).
49. 4 Vanderbilt L. R. 1 (1950) at 43.
50. An excellent account is found in Albert Deutsch's volume *The Mentally Ill in America,* 2nd ed., 1949.
51. Acts of 1797, ch. 62.
52. 3 Am. Law Rev. 193.
53. Hartford, 1873 (2 volumes).
54. Am. J. Insanity 69:571 (1913).
55. N. M. Stat. (1941), §§ 37-202, 37-203.
56. *Loc cit.* (note 52).
57. W. Overholser, "The Voluntary Admission Law," Am. J. Psych. 3:475 (1924).
58. Ex parte Romero, 51 N.M. 201, 181 P 2nd 811 (1947).
59. For example: Colby v. Jackson, 12 N.H. 526 (1842); Look v. Dean, 108 Mass. 116 (1871); In re Allen, 82 Vt. 365 (1909); Christiansen v. Weston, 36 Ariz. 200, 284 Pac. 149 (1930).
60. "Analysis of Legal and Medical Considerations in Commitment of the Mentally Ill," 56 Yale L. J. 1178 (1947).
61. Fowler v. Fowler, 219 Ala. 453, 122 So. 442 (1929).
62. 31 J. Am. Judicature Soc. 47 (1947). A good general discus-

sion of the proper approach to the problem is found in "Commitment of the Mentally Ill: Treatment or Travesty?" by Don H. Melaney, 12 U. of Pittsburgh L. R. 52 (1950).

63. In re Brewer, 224 Ia. 773, 276 N.W. 766 (1937).

64. G. L. (ter. ed.) c. 123, sec. 79.

65. Shields v. Shields, 26 F. Supp. 211 (1939). Another clear disregard of existing law is reported in Kelly v. Kipp et al., 77 Mont. 110, 250 Pac. 819 (1926).

66. For a discussion of this point, see comment, 47 Northwestern Univ. L. R. 100 (1952).

67. Kendall v. May, 10 Allen 59 (Mass. 1865); Leggate v. Clark, 111 Mass. 308 (1873); Tucker v. Am. Surety Co. 78 Ga. App. 327, 50 S.E. 2nd 859 (1948).

68. Mass. G. L. (ter. ed.) c. 123, sec. 101.

69. For a critique of this statute, see L. Harris and E. Gordon, 30 Boston Univ. L. R. 459 (1950).

70. These groups are discussed in "Commitment of the Mentally Ill," H. Weihofen and W. Overholser, 24 Texas L. R. 307 (1946), at 324-331.

71. Murray v. Murray, 313 Mass. 8, 45 N.E. 2nd 933 (1943).

72. Dodrer v. Dodrer, 183 Md. 413, 37 Atl. 2nd 919 (1944).

73. Dorsey v. Gill, 148 F 2nd 857 (1945); overruled, Overholser v. Boddie, 184 F 2nd 240 (1950).

74. Dorsey v. Gill, Supra.

75. For a discussion of this point, see H. Weihofen and W. Overholser, *op. cit.* (note 70), at 346.

76. *Mental Health Programs of the 48 States.* Chicago: Council of State Governments.

77. Several such cases are discussed in the Insurance Law J., No. 301, p. 106 (1948): M. M. Leichter, "The Mental Case, a Problem in Damages."

78. H. M. Pollock, *Mental Disease and Social Welfare*, ch. 16. Utica, 1941: State Hospitals Press.

79. L. H. Cohen and H. Freeman, Conn. St. Med. J. 9:697 (1945).

80. New York Times, July 29, 1952.

81. For a full discussion of this proposed act, see C. W. Whit-

more, 19 Geo. Wash. L. R. 512 (1951), and H. Weihofen, "Hospitalizing the Mentally Ill," 50 Mich. L. R. 837 (1952).

82. 73 Am. Bar Assn. Rep. 297 (1948).

83. R. v. Cullender and Duny, 6 How St. Tr. 687.

84. Fleet v. Metropolitan Asylums Board, 2 Times Law Rep. 361 (England).

85. In a recent land-damage case against the United States government, for example, the experts for the government valued the land at 70-75 cents per square foot, while the owner's experts set the value as "$2.50 up to $6.00" per square foot. The jury found the value at $1.45—about halfway between the two estimates! U.S. v. 25 Acres, 172 F 2nd 990 (1949).

86. Tracy Peerage Case, 10 Cl. & F. 154 (1843).

87. 10 U. of Chicago L. R. 285 (1943).

88. The court may even reverse itself and prevent further questions when the testimony shows the alleged expert to be incompetent. Carbonneau v. Lachance, 307 Mass. 153, 29 N.E. 2nd 696 (1940).

89. Kabai v. Majestic Collieries Co., 293 Ky. 783, 170 S.W. 2nd 357 (1943).

90. Shearn v. Anderson, —— S. D. ——, 48 N.W. 2nd 821 (1951).

91. Peo. v. Bobczyk, 343 Ill. App. 504, 99 N.E. 2nd 567 (1951).

92. See discussion by C. T. McCormick, "Some Observations Upon the Opinion Rule and Expert Testimony," 23 Texas L. R. 109 (1945).

93. 30 J. Crim. Law and Criminology 425 (1939).

94. See, for example, U.S. v. Hoxsey Cancer Clinic, 198 F 2nd 273 (1952).

95. B. & O. R.R. v. Schultz, 43 Ohio 271, 1 N.E. 324 (1885).

96. In re Dolbeer's Estate, 149 Cal. 227, 86 Pac. 695 (1906).

97. St. v. David, 222 N.C. 242, 22 S.E. 2nd 633 (1942).

98. Ferguson v. Hubbell, 97 N.Y. 507 (1884).

99. See, for more detailed study of this phase, W. Overholser, "Psychiatric Expert Testimony Since McNaghten—a Review," 42 J. Crim. Law 283 (1951). See also H. W. Taft, 14 Va. L. R. 81 (1927).

100. Sizer v. Burt, 4 Denio 426 (New York, 1847).

101. Strasburg v. St., 60 Wash. 106 (1910).

102. 5 J. Crim. Law 643 (1915). 6 *idem* 672 (1916).

103. Jessner v. St., 202 Wis. 184, 231 N.W. 634 (1930).

104. Mass. Gen. Laws, ter. ed. (as amended), c. 123, sec. 100 A. For a full discussion, see W. Overholser, "The Briggs Law of Massachusetts—a Review and an Appraisal," 25 J. Crim. Law 859 (1935).

105. Comm. v. Devereaux, 257 Mass. 391, 153 N.E. 881 (1926).

106. Peter J. Hagopian, "Mental Abnormalities in Criminals Based on Briggs Law Cases," Am. J. Psychiatry, 109:486 (1953).

107. Peo. v. Wolfe, 102 N.Y.S. 2nd 12 (1950), 103 *idem* 479 (1950), 105 *idem* 594 (1952). Comment, 12 U. of Pittsburgh L. R. 629 (1951).

108. Peo. v. Samuran, 408 Ill. 549, 97 N.E. 2nd 778 (1951).

109. Bowring v. Del. Rayon Co., 38 Del. 339, 192 Atl. 598 (1937).

110. Gen. Laws (ter. ed.), c. 123, sec. 99. Sullivan v. the Judges, 271 Mass. 435, 171 N.E. 490 (1930). For comment, see 16 Mass. L. Q. no. 6, p. 26 (May 1931) and 20 *idem*, no. 4, p. 23 (August 1935).

111. Sustained in Tunney v. Crosby, 112 Vt. 95, 22 Atl. 2nd 145 (1941).

112. Tyler v. Tyler, 401 Ill. 435, 82 N.E. 2nd 346 (1948).

113. Holland v. St., 80 Tex. Cr. App. Rep. 637, 192 S.W. 1070 (1917).

114. See remarks of Sir George Jessel, Master of the Rolls, in Thorn v. Worthing Skating Rink Co., 6 Chancery Div. 415 (1876).

115. H. M. Stephens, "What Courts Can Learn from Commissions," 19 A.B.A.J. 141 (1933).

116. "Truth in the Evaluation of Crime," Keith Simpson. Medico Legal Journal (London) 16:27, Part I, 1948.

117. Am. J. Insanity 31:277 (1875).

118. See E. M. Hammes, "Eight Years' Experience with the Control of Medical Expert Testimony," J. Omaha Mid-West Clin. Soc. 10:13 (1949).

INDEX

[145]